£5.99

Practice Papers for SQA Exams

Higher

Physics

ISBN 978-1-84372-784-2

Published by
Leckie & Leckie Ltd, 4 Queen Street, Edinburgh, EH2 1JE
Tel: 0131 220 6831 Fax: 0131 225 9987
enquiries@leckieandleckie.co.uk   www.leckieandleckie.co.uk

A CIP Catalogue record for this book is available from the British Library.

Leckie & Leckie Ltd is a division of Huveaux plc.

Questions and answers in this book do not emanate from SQA. All of our entirely new and original Practice Papers have been written by experienced authors working directly for the publisher.

Introduction

Layout of the Book

This book contains practice exam papers, which mirror the actual SQA exam. The layout, paper colour and question level are all similar to the actual exam that you will sit, so that you are familiar with what the exam paper will look like.

The answer section is at the back of the book. The box at the start of each answer gives some general tips and formulae. If you are struggling to find the answer, why not use them as a hint? Then, if you still have problems, go to the solution.

Revision advice is provided in this introductory section of the book, so please read on!

How To Use This Book

The Practice Papers can be used in two main ways:

1. You can complete an entire practice paper as preparation for the final exam. If you would like to use the book in this way, you can either complete the practice paper under exam style conditions by setting yourself a time for each paper and answering it as well as possible without using any references or notes. Alternatively, you can answer the practice paper questions as a revision exercise, using your notes to produce a model answer. Your teacher may mark these for you.

2. You can use the Topic Index on page 5 to find all the questions within the book that deal with a specific topic. This allows you to focus specifically on areas that you particularly want to revise or, if you are mid-way through your course, it lets you practice answering exam-style questions for just those topics that you have studied.

Revision Advice

Work out a revision timetable for each week's work in advance – remember to cover all of your subjects and to leave time for homework and breaks. For example:

Day	6pm–6.45pm	7pm–8pm	8.15pm–9pm	9.15pm–10pm
Monday	Homework	Homework	English Revision	Chemistry Revision
Tuesday	Maths Revision	Physics Revision	Homework	Free
Wednesday	Geography Revision	Modern Studies Revision	English Revision	French Revision
Thursday	Homework	Maths Revision	Chemistry Revision	Free
Friday	Geography Revision	French Revision	Free	Free
Saturday	Free	Free	Free	Free
Sunday	Modern Studies Revision	Maths Revision	Modern Studies Revision	Homework

Make sure that you have at least one evening free a week to relax, socialise and re-charge your batteries. It also gives your brain a chance to process the information that you have been feeding it all week.

Arrange your study time into one hour or 30 minute sessions, with a break between sessions e.g. 6 pm–7 pm, 7.15 pm–7.45 pm, 8 pm–9 pm. Try to start studying as early as possible in the evening when your brain is still alert and be aware that the longer you put off starting, the harder it will be to start!

Study a different subject in each session, except in the days before an exam.

Do something different during your breaks between study sessions – have a cup of tea, or listen to some music. Don't let your 15 minutes expand into 20 or 25 minutes though!

Have your class notes and any textbooks available for your revision to hand as well as plenty of blank paper, a pen, etc.

Finally forget or ignore all or some of the advice in this section if you are happy with your present way of studying. Everyone revises differently, so find a way that works for you!

In the Exam

Watch your time and pace yourself carefully. Work out roughly how much time you can spend on each answer and try to stick to this. You have 2½ hours to tackle the exam of 90 marks so that's just over half an hour for the multiple-choice paper and about 2 hours for the written extended answer questions. Read the instructions carefully and don't forget that data such as the speed of light, Planck's constant, etc., are on a page near the front of the paper. They are not generally included in each question.

Read the question thoroughly before you begin to answer it – make sure you know exactly what the question is asking you to do. Most physics questions involve the use of a **formula**, either to calculate a numerical answer or to form the basis of an explanation. The formulae are available to you in an SQA booklet but you really should try to learn them. Use the booklet as a 'back-up'.

Topic Index

Topics	Exam A	Exam B	Exam C
Kinematics, equations of motion. Speed, distance, time. v/t graphs	1	1, 2b, 2d	1d, 2a
Vectors, scalars, components	2e	1, 2c	1c
Forces, F = ma, force as a vector, tension. Weight, mg. momentum change	2, 3	3b, 3d	2b, 2c
Mechanical energy			1a, 1b, 2d
Buoyancy, flotation, upthrust. Pressure/density in liquids and gases	3	3	
Gas Laws. Kinetic model of gases			3
Charged particles in electric fields $qV = \frac{1}{2}mv^2$; $Q = It$	9e		4a, 4b
DC circuits, potential dividers, V = IR	4		
Power			4c, 5c, 5d, 7b
Internal resistance	5	4a, 4b	5
DC capacitors	6	5	
ac, V_{peak}, V_{rms}, frequency, CRO patterns. Capacitor in ac	7c	3a, 6	6c
Operational amplifier	7	4c(ii)	6
mosfet	7d	4c(i)	
Refraction of light, refractive index, colour. $v = f\lambda$		7	
Diffraction of light, colour	8a, 8b	8	
Interference, $v = f\lambda$			8
LED, E = hf			7
Photoelectric effect, photons	9		9a
Fusion		9	
Radiation and safety, dose, activity			9
Uncertainties	8c		2e, 8c

Data Sheet

Refractive Indices

The refractive indices refer to sodium light of wavelength 589 nm and to substances at a temperature of 273 K.

Substance	Refractive index	Substance	Refractive index
Crown glass	1·50	Air	1·00
Water	1·33		

Common Physical Quantities

Quantity	Symbol	Value	Quantity	Symbol	Value
Speed of light in vacuum	c	$3 \cdot 00 \times 10^{8}\,\text{ms}^{-1}$	Mass of electron	m_e	$9 \cdot 11 \times 10^{-31}\,\text{kg}$
Magnitude of the charge on an electron	e	$1 \cdot 60 \times 10^{-19}\,\text{C}$	Mass of neutron	m_n	$1 \cdot 675 \times 10^{-27}\,\text{kg}$
Gravitational acceleration on Earth	g	$9 \cdot 8\,\text{ms}^{-2}$	Mass of proton	m_p	$1 \cdot 673 \times 10^{-27}\,\text{kg}$
Planck's constant	h	$6 \cdot 63 \times 10^{-34}\,\text{Js}$			

Spectral Lines

Element	Wavelength/nm	Colour
Hydrogen	656	Red
	486	Blue-green
	434	Blue-violet
	410	Violet
	397	Ultraviolet
	389	Ultraviolet
Sodium	589	Yellow

Properties of selected materials

Substance	Density/kg m^{-3}	Melting Point/K	Boiling Point/K
Ice	$9 \cdot 20 \times 10^{2}$	273	....
Sea Water	$1 \cdot 02 \times 10^{3}$	264	377
Water	$1 \cdot 00 \times 10^{3}$	273	373
Air	$1 \cdot 29$	....	....
Hydrogen	$9 \cdot 0 \times 10^{-2}$	14	20

The gas densities refer to a temperature of 273 K and a pressure of $1 \cdot 01 \times 10^{5}\,\text{Pa}$

Practice Exam A

Physics   Higher

Practice Papers
For SQA Exams

Exam A

You are allowed 2 hours, 30 minutes to complete this paper.

Try to answer all of the questions.

Part 1 has 20 questions.
Each question in Part 1 is worth 1 mark.
For each question there are 5 possible answers shown (labelled A-E). In each
question, only one of these options is the correct answer.

Part 2 has 10 extended response questions.
The total marks available in this part of the exam is 70.
Include any appropriate working in your answer, but make sure that your final answer
for each question is clear.
Where it is necessary, remember to include the correct number of significant figures
in your answers to calculations.

Leckie × Leckie

Scotland's leading educational publishers

PART 1

1. Which of the following are both scalar quantities?

   A   Energy and speed

   B   Impulse and energy

   C   Displacement and momentum

   D   Weight and speed

   E   Acceleration and force   1

2. The graph shows a velocity—time curve for a car moving off from rest

   An acceleration-time graph for the car over the same time interval could be :-

   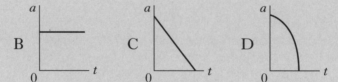   1

3. A plane flying horizontally at 200 ms⁻¹ releases a bomb from a height of 78·4 m. Neglecting air resistance, the bomb will hit the target if the distance x is :-

   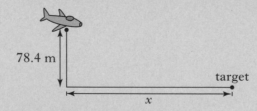

   A   78·4 m

   B   200 m

   C   400 m

   D   800 m

   E   1600 m   1

4. A force of 69 N is used to pull a 10 kg mass up a 30° slope. The mass moves up the slope with an acceleration of 1·5 ms⁻².

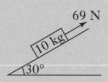

The size of the friction force opposing the motion is :-

A   5 N

B   10 N

C   20 N

D   49 N

E   59 N   1

5. A 1 kg object is acted on by a force which changes as shown in the graph below:-

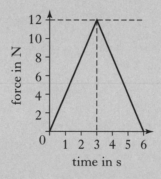

The change in momentum of the object is :-

A   6 kg ms⁻¹

B   12 kg ms⁻¹

C   18 kg ms⁻¹

D   36 kg ms⁻¹

E   72 kg ms⁻¹   1

6. A pellet is fired into a hanging lump of plasticine and sticks inside it. The lump moves off at 2 ms^{-1}. Through what vertical height, h, does the plasticine rise?

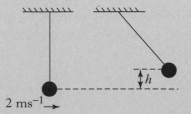

A   0·10 m

B   0·20 m

C   0·30 m

D   0·40 m

E   0·45 m   1

7. A fixed mass of gas has a volume of 2 m^3. If the pressure on the gas is doubled and the kelvin temperature is also doubled the new volume will be :-

A   0·5 m^3

B   1·0 m^3

C   1·2 m^3

D   2·0 m^3

E   4·0 m^3 1

8. A sample of nitrogen gas has a volume of 1000 cm^3. The sample is placed in a pressure vessel and converted to a liquid. The volume of this liquid will be approximately :-

A   1000 cm^3

B   100 cm^3

C   10 cm^3

D   1 cm^3

E   0·1 cm^3 1

9. Electrons at rest in a vacuum tube are accelerated from the cathode to the anode by a p.d. of 1000 V.
   If the p.d. was increased to 4000 V the electrons would reach the anode with :-

   A   Four times the speed and four times the kinetic energy.

   B   Twice the speed and four times the kinetic energy.

   C   Twice the speed and twice the kinetic energy.

   D   Four times the speed and twice the kinetic energy.

   E   Half the speed and half the kinetic energy.   1

10. In the following circuits each **cell** has the same emf and negligible internal resistance and the resistors are all of the same value. Which two ammeters will show the same reading?

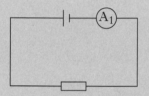 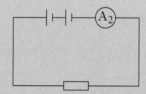 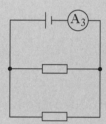

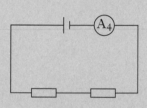 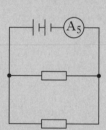

   A   A$_1$ and A$_2$

   B   A$_1$ and A$_3$

   C   A$_2$ and A$_3$

   D   A$_3$ and A$_4$

   E   A$_2$ and A$_5$ 1

11. The emf of the cell in the following circuit is 1·6 V. The cell has an internal resistance. The reading on the voltmeter is 1·2 V. The ammeter reading will be :-

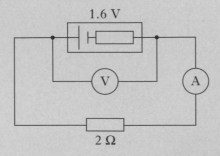

1.6 V

2 Ω

A 0·2 A

B 0·4 A

C 0·6 A

D 0·8 A   1

E 1·0 A

12. An a.c. supply produces a constant voltage. The frequency of the supply can be varied.

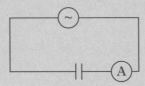

Which of the graphs below correctly shows the variation in current as the frequency is increased?

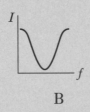

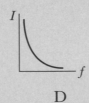
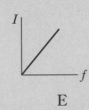

A   B   C   D   E   1

13. An oscilloscope has its timebase switched off and its Y gain set to 5 V per division. The screen is shown below.

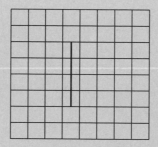

The voltage shown is :-

A   5 V dc

B   5 V peak ac

C   10 V dc

D   10 V peak ac

E   20 V peak ac   1

14. The circuit below is used to produce square waves. The input voltage is 5 V ac.

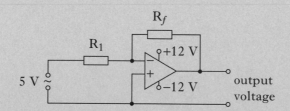

Which values of resistors R_1 and R_f will produce a square wave?

	R_1 (kΩ)	R_f (kΩ)
A	20	1
B	20	5
C	20	10
D	10	20
E	1	20

1

15. Two plane mirrors are placed at 60° to each other as shown below. A ray of light strikes mirror 1 at an angle of incidence of 20°

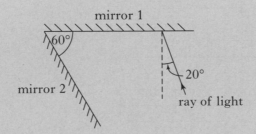

The angle of reflection at mirror 2 will be :-

A   20°

B   30°

C   40°

D   50°

E   60°

1

16. The diagram shows a ray of light passing through a semicircular plastic block.

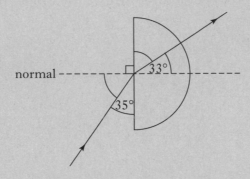

The refractive index of the glass is :-

A $\dfrac{\sin 35°}{\sin 33°}$

B $\dfrac{\sin 33°}{\sin 35°}$

C $\dfrac{\sin 33°}{\sin 55°}$

D $\dfrac{\sin 55°}{\sin 57°}$

E $\dfrac{\sin 55°}{\sin 33°}$

1

17.

In a demonstration of diffraction a pattern of bright spots and dark areas is produced on a screen. The distance between the bright spots could be increased by :-

A   using a light source of lower frequency.

B   replacing the grating with one of greater slit separation.

C   decreasing the distance between grating and screen.

D   using a light source of shorter wavelength.

E   decreasing the distance between light source and grating.   1

18. The diagram represents different electron energy levels in an atom. The energy values are shown in units. The arrows show five possible electron transitions. Which transition would produce light of the longest wavelength?

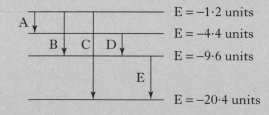

1

19. The irradiance of a point source of light is 36 W m^{-2} at a distance of 2 m from the source. The irradiance at a distance of 6 m will be :-

A   36 Wm^{-2}

B   18 Wm^{-2}

C   6 Wm^{-2}

D   4 Wm^{-2}

E   3 Wm^{-2} 1

20. Which row in the table correctly shows the units for all three radiation quantities?

	Activity	Absorbed Dose	Equivalent Dose
A	becquerel	joule	gray
B	gray	joule	sievert
C	becquerel	gray	sievert
D	second	sievert	gray
E	sievert	gray	joule

1

PART 2

A1. Two young runners are practising sprint starts with their coach.

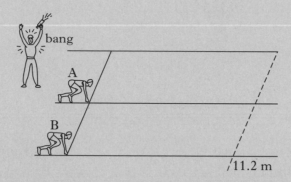

Runner A has a reaction time of 0·26s. He can maintain an acceleration of 1·6 ms⁻². Runner B reacts in a time of 0·20s but his acceleration is only 1·4 ms⁻². When the starting gun is fired, they run until they pass a marker on the ground 11·2 m away.

(*a*) Show that A reaches the marker 0·20s ahead of B. Working should be shown clearly. **3**

(*b*) How fast is B travelling when he reaches the marker? **2**

(*c*) If B continues at this speed until he completes a total distance of 60 m, show that his total time for the sprint is 12·9s. **2**

A2.

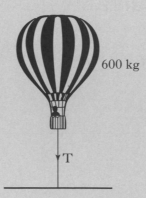

A hot air balloon has just been inflated and is tethered to the ground by a rope. The total mass of the balloon is 600 kg.

(a) What is the weight of the balloon? **2**

(b) The upthrust on the balloon is 6180 N. What causes this upthrust? **2**

(c) Find the tension in the rope while the balloon remains tethered. **2**

(d) If the balloon was released, calculate the value of its acceleration. **2**

(e) Just before release, a light, steady breeze blows from the west and causes the rope to be displaced 10° from the vertical. Show that the tension in the rope would increase to 304·6 N. **2**

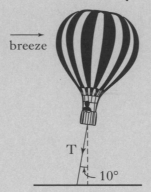

A3. A pupil experiments with a method of measuring the densities of liquids using a clear plastic container. He marks a centimetre scale on the side and places some iron filings inside. The total mass of the container and filings is 50 g. The cross-sectional area of the base is 5 cm² (5×10^{-4} m²)

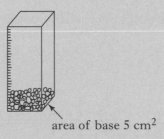

area of base 5 cm²

The container is placed in water; it sinks to a depth of 10 cm and floats as shown.

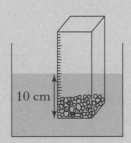

10 cm

(*a*) What is the upthrust (in newtons) on the base of the container?   **1**

(*b*) Calculate the upwards pressure of the water on the base of the container.   **2**

(*c*) Use your answer to part (c) to show clearly that the density of the water is 1000 kg m⁻³.   **2**

(*d*) To what depth would the container sink if it was placed in a liquid twice as dense as water?   **1**

A4. Two pupils were given a 12 volt supply and some resistors and asked to construct a potential divider circuit capable of operating a light bulb rated at 3 V; 0·9 W

(a) When operating correctly, what would be the bulb's resistance?   **2**

(b) The first pupil set up circuit 1 and successfully connected and lit the bulb.

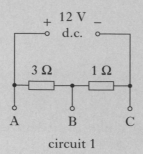

circuit 1

Explain in which position (AB or BC) the bulb should be connected to light at near normal brightness.   **2**

(c) The second pupil set up circuit 2 and then connected the bulb across AB. All the components were working properly but the bulb brightness was very low. Explain why this circuit is not appropriate.   **2**

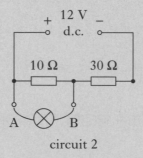

circuit 2

A5. The following circuit was used to determine the internal resistance, r, of a dry cell.

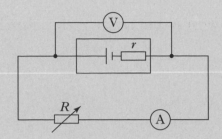

Voltmeter and ammeter readings were taken and shown in the table below :-

V (volts)	I (amperes)
0·70	0·70
1·05	0·35
1·17	0·23
1·23	0·18
1·26	0·14

(a) Starting with the equation $E = V_{tpd} + V_{lost}$

show that $V_{tpd} = -r\,(I) + E$　　　　　　　　　　　1

(b) Draw a suitable graph of the results and from it determine values for the emf of the cell and its internal resistance.　　　4

(c) Show that the short circuit current of the cell is 1·4A.　　　2

A6.

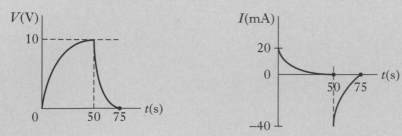

The graphs above were obtained from the ammeter and voltmeter readings in the circuit shown. Switch S was first connected to point X and when the capacitor was fully charged after 50 seconds, the switch was immediately connected to point Y.

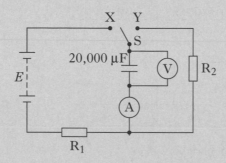

(a) Calculate the value of resistor R_1.   2

(b) Give two reasons why the resistance of R_2 will be smaller than the resistance of R_1.   2

(c) Calculate the final charge stored on the capacitor.   2

(d) Show that the average value of the discharge current is 8 mA.   2

A7.

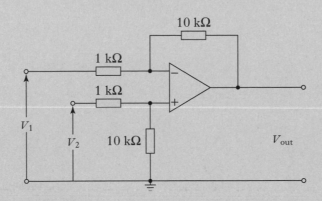

A pupil sets up the operational amplifier circuit shown above.

(a) In which mode is the amplifier operating? **1**

(b) What is the gain of the amplifier? **1**

(c) The pupil connects oscilloscopes across V_1 and V_{out}. The displays on the screens are shown below :-

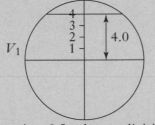

y gain = 0.5 volts per division

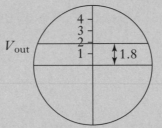

y gain = 5.0 volts per division

Use the information to calculate the voltage V_2. **3**

(d) The output V_{out} of the amplifier is connected to a semiconductor device which acts to switch on a lamp.

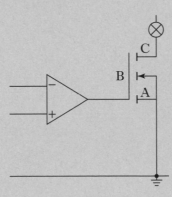

(i) Name the device.

(ii) Name the three parts of the device A, B and C. **2**

A8.

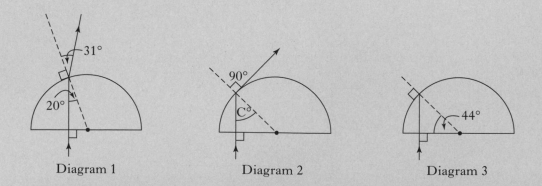

| Diagram 1 | Diagram 2 | Diagram 3 |

The diagrams above, taken from a pupil's notes, show a ray of red light passing into a semicircular glass block.

(a) Use the information in diagrams 1 and 2 to find

  (i) the refractive index of the glass   **2**

  (ii) the value of angle C°   **2**

(b) Make a sketch of diagram 3 and complete it to show the first change of direction of the ray of light.
Mark any relevant angles on your sketch.   **2**

A9.

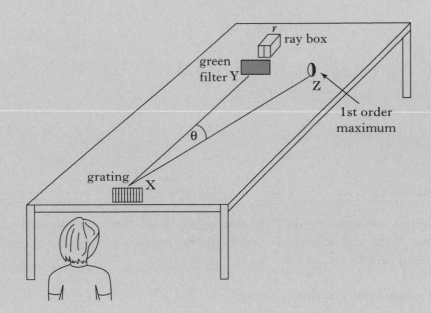

A class is asked to use a 300 lines per mm diffraction grating with a ray box and green filter to calculate a value for the wavelength of green light. One pupil sets up the equipment as shown and with the help of a friend locates the first order maximum at Z. Distance XZ-200 cm and YZ = 30 cm.

(a) Calculate her value for the wavelength of green light. Express your answer in nanometres.

3

(b) Seven pupils then repeat the experiment with the green filter. Their values are listed below. Use the seven results to quote a value for the wavelength of green light with its uncertainty.

λ (nm) 511, 505, 500, 496, 509, 490, 503.

2

A10.

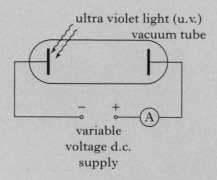

Ultraviolet radiation passes through the special glass of the vacuum tube and liberates electrons from the metal electrode in the apparatus shown above. A current is registered on the ammeter.

(a) What is the name given to this process? **1**

(b) The wavelength of the u.v. radiation is 300 nm. Calculate the energy of a u.v. photon. **2**

(c) The work function of the metal is $4 \cdot 23 \times 10^{-19}$ J. Calculate the kinetic energy of an electron liberated from the metal by a u.v. photon. **2**

(d) If the terminals of the voltage supply are reversed, the ammeter may still register a current. Explain why this happens. **1**

(e) Show that a reversed voltage of $1 \cdot 5$V is necessary to bring the current to zero. **2**

[End of Question Paper]

Practice Exam B

Physics   Higher

Practice Papers
For SQA Exams   **Exam B**

You are allowed 2 hours, 30 minutes to complete this paper.

Try to answer all of the questions.

Part 1 has 20 questions.
Each question in Part 1 is worth 1 mark.
For each question there are 5 possible answers shown (labelled A-E). In each
question, only one of these options is the correct answer.

Part 2 has 10 extended response questions.
The total marks available in this part of the exam is 70.
Include any appropriate working in your answer, but make sure that your final answer
for each question is clear.
Where it is necessary, remember to include the correct number of significant figures
in your answers to calculations.

Leckie×Leckie
Scotland's leading educational publishers

PAPER B

1. A pupil uses the equipment shown below to make measurements of length, time and temperature :-

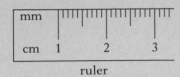
ruler

celsius
thermometer

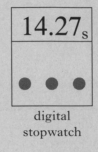
digital
stopwatch

Which measurement would have the largest percentage scale reading uncertainty?

A   A time of 1·00 s.

B   A time of 10 s.

C   A temperature of 5 °C.

D   A length of 3 cm.

E   A length of 2 mm.   1

2. The displacement-time graph for a moving object is shown below

Which of the following graphs could represent the same motion?

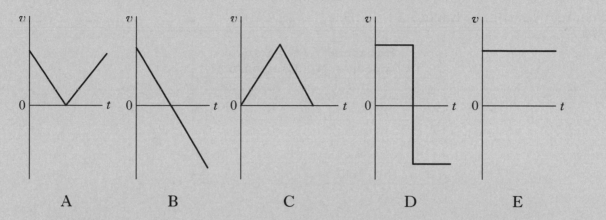

A   B   C   D   E

1

3. A ball is projected horizontally from the top of a tall building with a speed of 10 ms⁻¹. Neglecting air resistance, its speed after 2 s should be :-

A   5 ms^{-1}

B   10 ms^{-1}

C   19·6 ms^{-1}

D   20 ms^{-1}

E   22 ms^{-1}

1

4. A 10 N force acts on the block of wood shown below.

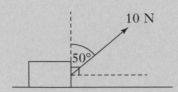

Which row in the table gives correct values for both the horizontal and vertical components of the force?

	Horizontal Component (N)	Vertical Component (N)
A	10 sin 50°	10 cos 50°
B	10 cos 40°	10 sin 40°
C	10 cos 40°	10 sin 50°
D	10 cos 50°	10 sin 50°
E	10 sin 40°	10 cos 40°

1

5. A 2 kg model lorry is travelling along a horizontal surface at 2 ms⁻¹. A 2 kg load of sand falls vertically downwards on to the lorry as shown below.

If friction forces can be neglected, how do the momentum and the kinetic energy of the loaded lorry compare with those of the empty lorry?

	Momentum	Kinetic Energy
A	same	same
B	same	doubled
C	same	halved
D	halved	halved
E	halved	same

1

6.

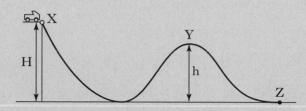

A small toy car is released from point X and travels down the track past Y to reach Z. Neglecting friction, the kinetic energy of the car at Y will be :-

A   mg H

B   mg h

C   mg (h – II)

D   mg (H + h)

E   mg (H – h)   **1**

7. The graph below was drawn by a pupil who performed a successful experiment to verify one of the three Gas Laws. Unfortunately, he forgot to label the physical quantities on the x and y axes.

Which row in the table could show correct labels for both axes?

	x axis	y axis
A	Temperature (°C)	Volume
B	Temperature (°C)	$\dfrac{1}{\text{Volume}}$
C	Temperature (°C)	Pressure
D	Volume	Pressure
E	$\dfrac{1}{\text{Volume}}$	Pressure

1

8.

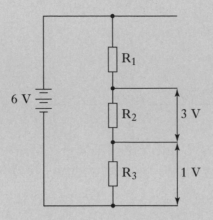

This circuit provides voltages of 3 V or 1 V from a 6 V supply. Which row in the table below gives correct values of resistance for R_1, R_2 and R_3?

	R_1 (kΩ)	R_2 (kΩ)	R_3 (kΩ)
A	2	6	2
B	6	2	6
C	4	2	6
D	4	6	2
E	2	6	4

1

9. The circuit shows a cell with internal resistance r connected to a light bulb of resistance R. The fraction of the total power dissipated by the bulb is :-

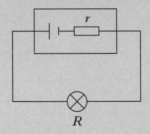

A $\dfrac{R}{r}$

B $\dfrac{r}{R}$

C $\dfrac{R + r}{r}$

D $\dfrac{R}{R + r}$

E $\dfrac{r}{R + r}$

10. Which of the following units is equivalent to a farad?

A JC^{-1}

B CJ^{-1}

C CV^{-1}

D VC^{-1}

E CV

           1

11. In the circuit below, the 10,000 μF capacitor has a charge of 0·1C on its plates.

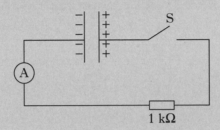

When the switch S is closed the current-time graph is :-

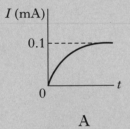

A

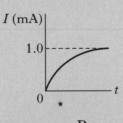

B

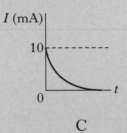

C

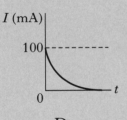

D

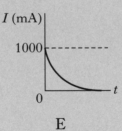

E

           1

12. The waveform on this oscilloscope has a frequency of 100 Hz.

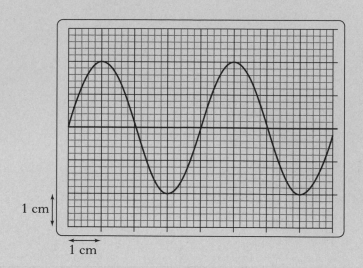

1 cm

1 cm

The timebase setting is :-

A   2·5 ms per cm

B   5·0 ms per cm

C   10 ms per cm

D   25 ms per cm

E   25 ms per cm   1

13.

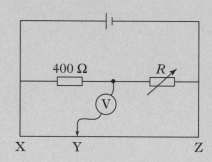

In the Wheatstone Bridge circuit, wire XZ is 100 cm long. The bridge is balanced when length YZ is 60 cm. If variable resistor R is doubled in value, the new balance will occur when length YZ is :-

A   25 cm

B   40 cm

C   60 cm

D   75 cm

E   80 cm   1

14. Which statement correctly describes the situation of the LED in this circuit?

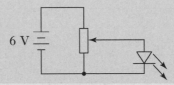

A   It does not light because there is no p.d. across it.

B   It does not light because it is forward biased.

C   It does not light because it is reverse biased.

D   It lights because it is forward biased.

E   It lights because it is reverse biased.

1

15. A ray of light of wavelength 650 nm and frequency $4 \cdot 62 \times 10$ in air passes into a liquid of refractive index $1 \cdot 3$. Which row in the table shows correct values for wavelength and frequency in both air and liquid?

	λ liquid (nm)	f liquid (Hz)
A	500	$3 \cdot 55 \times 10^{14}$
B	500	$4 \cdot 62 \times 10^{14}$
C	845	$4 \cdot 62 \times 10^{14}$
D	845	$6 \cdot 00 \times 10^{14}$
E	845	$3 \cdot 55 \times 10^{14}$

1

16. A diffraction pattern is produced when light passes though a grating. The first order maximum is produced at angle θ.

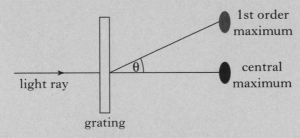

Which row in the table below gives the combination of wavelength and lines on the grating which would produce the smallest value of θ?

	Wavelength (nm)	Grating lines per (mm)
A	400	300
B	400	600
C	500	300
D	600	600
E	700	600

1

17. The diagram shows three energy levels for electrons in an atom. E_0 is the lowest level.

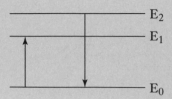

If transition E_0 to E_1 represents absorption of green light, then transition E_2 to E_0 could represent

A   absorption of blue light

B   absorption of red light

C   emission of blue light

D   emission of red light

E   emission of infra red   1

18. The irradiance of a gamma source can be measured in

A   Bq

B   Sv

C   W

D Wm^{-2}

E   Gy   1

19. A raybox with a violet filter is used to produce a photoelectric current in the circuit below.

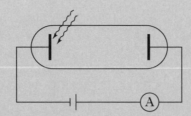

The brightness of the raybox lamp is increased. Which row in the table correctly shows the effect of this increase?

	Ammeter reading	Kinetic energy of each photoelectron
A	decreased	decreased
B	unchanged	unchanged
C	unchanged	decreased
D	increased	unchanged
E	increased	increased

1

20. The process by which $^{238}_{92}$U changes to $^{234}_{90}$Th is called :-

A   spontaneous fission

B   induced fission

C   alpha decay

D   beta decay

E   nuclear fusion

1

PART 2

B1.

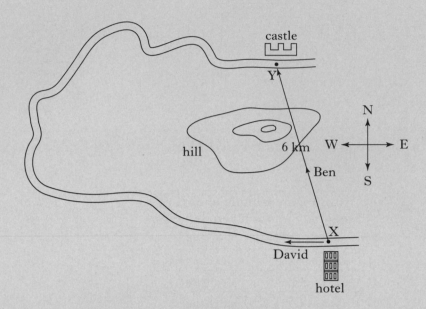

Two cyclists, Ben and David, decide to race from their hotel to a nearly castle. They start together. David cycles round the road shown on the map above from X to Y. Ben cycles directly across the hillside in a 6 km straight line from X to Y. He arrives 5 minutes ahead of David. Ben uses the map and his watch to calculate his average velocity as 8 km h^{-1} bearing 350°. David's bike computer records a distance of 25 km for his journey.

(a) Explain the difference between a vector and a scalar. **1**

(b) What is David's displacement for the journey from X to Y? **1**

(c) What is David's average velocity (in km h^{-1}) for the journey? **3**

(d) The boys swap over the routes for the return journey. Ben takes exactly one hour for the road journey. What is his average velocity? **1**

B2.

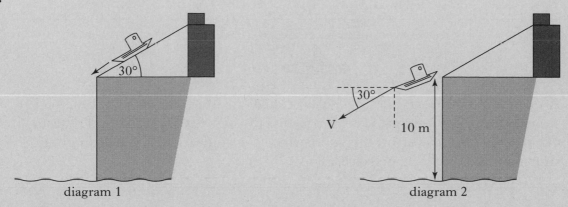

diagram 1   diagram 2

The diagrams show the launch from an oil rig of a "freefall" lifeboat. The boat slides down the 30° ramp from rest in one second, then falls as a projectile to the sea. You may neglect any frictional effects due to the ramp or the air.

(*a*) Calculate the acceleration of the lifeboat as it travels down the ramp (Diagram 1).   **2**

(*b*) How fast is the lifeboat travelling as it leaves the ramp? (Diagram 2)   **2**

(*c*) Calculate the vertical component of the boat's velocity as it leaves the ramp.   **2**

(*d*) The boat reaches the water 1·2s after leaving the ramp. Show that the vertical height fallen is 10 metres.   **2**

B3.

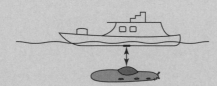

(a) A surface warship tests out its echo location device on a stationary submerged submarine. The sound pulse is transmitted through the sea water and reflects off the conning tower of the submarine. The pulse and its reflection are shown on the oscilloscope trace.

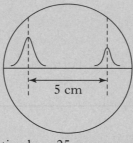

timebase 25 ms per cm

Using the information on the oscilloscope and taking the speed of sound as 1600 ms^{-1}, find how far that the submarine lies below the ship.

3

(b) The submarine has a mass of 10,000 tonnes (1 tonne = 1000 kg). Calculate the size of the buoyancy force (upthrust) on the submarine.

2

(c) Explain how this buoyancy force is produced.

1

(d) When the warship leaves, the submarine pumps 200 tonnes of sea water out of its tanks in order to surface. Calculate the resultant upward force on the submarine.

2

B4. Two cars travelling towards each other skid on a smooth level patch of ice and collide head on. They become entangled after the impact.

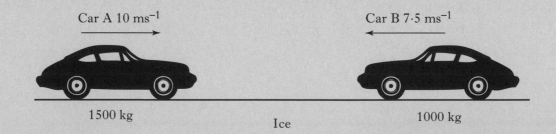

Car A 10 ms^{-1} Car B 7·5 ms^{-1}

1500 kg 1000 kg

Ice

(a) Calculate the velocity of the entangled cars immediately after the collision.

2

(b) Calculate the change in momentum of car B as a result of the collision.

2

(c) If the collision lasted for 2 seconds, find the force exerted on car B during the collision.

1

(d) What force was exerted on car A during the collision? Explain your answer with reference to one of Newton's laws.

2

B5. A pupil working on the design of a simple burglar alarm has two identical cells of emf 1·5 V and internal resistance 1 Ω. She connects one of them as shown in circuit 1. Circuit 1 has a switch S, which closes (switches on) when a window or door is opened :-

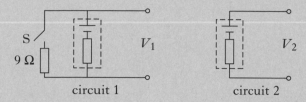

circuit 1   circuit 2

(a) What is the value of voltage V_2? **1**

(b) What is the value of voltage V_1 when :-

   (i) S is open **1**

   (ii) S is closed? **2**

(c) The girl plans to connect the two voltages into the following circuit :-

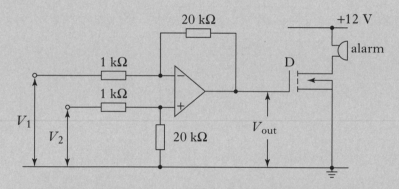

The semiconductor device labelled D will trigger the alarm if the output voltage is 2 V or more.

1

   (i) Name device D.

   (ii) By calculating the output voltage V_{out} show that a burglar who opened a window or a door would trigger the alarm. **2**

B6. A pupil designs and sets up the circuit below as a new method of finding the time taken for a ballbearing to fall a short distance, d. Two "gate" switches, S_1 and S_2, are made of aluminium foil. As the ballbearing falls it switches off S_1 then S_2.

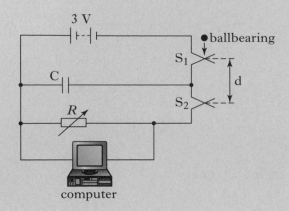

The pupil drops the ballbearing. He hopes to see a display like that of Fig. 1 on the computer screen.

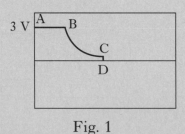

Fig. 1

(a) Explain the shapes of the three sections AB, BC and CD.   3

(b) Unfortunately his first few attempts produce the following pattern :-

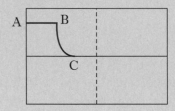

Describe how he could adjust the variable resistor to obtain a trace like Fig 1.   2

(c) Finally he has a successful attempt and obtains the following trace. Use the information to find the time for the ballbearing to fall distance d.

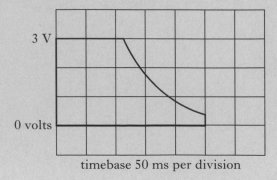

timebase 50 ms per division   1

B7. A variable frequency a.c. supply is connected to an oscilloscope. The display is shown below :-

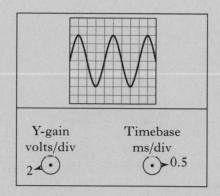

(a) Calculate   (i) the peak voltage   **1**

                (ii) the frequency of the a.c. waveform   **2**

(b) The supply is connected in the circuit below. The ammeters read rms values of the alternating current.

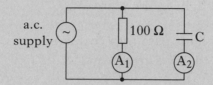

Calculate the reading on ammeter A_1.   **2**

(c) The voltage of the supply is kept constant but the frequency is doubled. Explain whether any changes would occur to the readings on ammeters A_1 and A_2.   **2**

B8. A specialist glass manufacturer produces this graph to show how the refractive index of his glass depends on the frequency of the light.

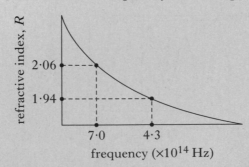

The numerical values shown are for red light and violet light.

(a) Using the values on the graph and any other data you require from the data sheet find :-

    (i)   the wavelength of red light in air   **2**

    (ii) the wavelength of red light in the glass   **2**

(b) Fine rays of red and violet light pass into two isosceles prisms made of the glass. Parts of the paths of the rays are shown.

    (i)   Show by calculation that beam A is red light and B is violet light.   **3**

    (ii) Find the size of angles y and z.   **2**

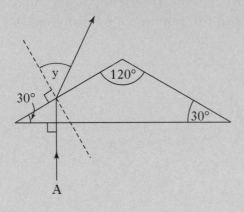

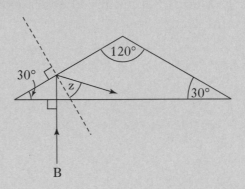

B9. A laser pointer contains both a red laser of frequency $4 \cdot 8 \times 10^{14}$ Hz and a green laser of frequency $6 \cdot 0 \times 10^{14}$ Hz. The lasers produce light by the process of stimulated emission.

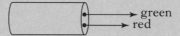

(a) Explain what is meant by the term 'stimulated emission'. **2**

(b) Both lasers are switched on. The laser beams travel to a screen several metres away and two coloured dots of light appear side by side at R and G.

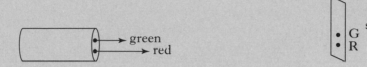

A grating of 600 lines per mm is then placed in front of the point. Two new dots now appear several centimetres apart at X and Y.

    (i) Calculate a value for the grating spacing, d, in metres. **2**

    (ii) Show that the dot at X is green and the dot at Y is red. **3**

B10. Research is currently taking place to design a nuclear fusion reactor using very high powered krypton-fluoride lasers. The lasers compress a "fuel" of deuterium and tritium to great density and heat it to millions of degrees.

The reaction is :-

$$^2_1H + ^3_1H \rightarrow ^4_2He + ^1_0n$$

(a) What is meant by the term "nuclear fusion"? **1**

(b) Use the masses of the constituents and any other data you require to calculate the energy released when the two nuclei fuse together :-

^2_1H $3 \cdot 342 \times 10^{-27}$ kg ^4_2He $6 \cdot 642 \times 10^{-27}$ kg

^3_1H $5 \cdot 005 \times 10^{-27}$ kg ^1_0n $1 \cdot 674 \times 10^{-27}$ kg   **3**

(c) The energy in a single laser pulse is $1 \cdot 5 \times 10^6$ J and the initial aim of the designers is to achieve a fusion output 100 times greater than the laser energy input. Show that one single laser pulse would have to trigger $5 \cdot 38 \times 10^{19}$ fusions to achieve this. **2**

[End of Question Paper]

Practice Exam C

Physics   Higher

Practice Papers
For SQA Exams   Exam C

You are allowed 2 hours, 30 minutes to complete this paper.

Try to answer all of the questions.

Part 1 has 20 questions.
Each question in Part 1 is worth 1 mark.
For each question there are 5 possible answers shown (labelled A-E). In each
question, only one of these options is the correct answer.

Part 2 has 10 extended response questions.
The total marks available in this part of the exam is 70.
Include any appropriate working in your answer, but make sure that your final answer
for each question is clear.
Where it is necessary, remember to include the correct number of significant figures
in your answers to calculations.

Leckie×Leckie
Scotland's leading educational publishers

PAPER C

1. Which of the following quantities can correctly be measured in newtons?

   A   Energy × time

   B   Momentum × time

   C   Energy × distance

   D   Momentum × distance

   E   Energy ÷ distance   **1**

2. Look at the following graphs :-

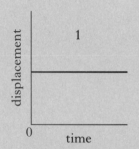 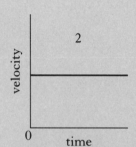 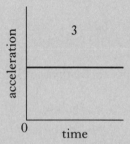

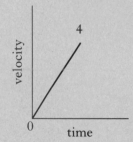 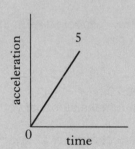

   Which pair of graphs could represent the same motion?

   A   1 and 2

   B   1 and 3

   C   2 and 5

   D   3 and 4

   E   4 and 5   **1**

3. A woman weighs 500 N. She stands on newton scales in a lift. The reading on the scales is 520 N. This shows that the lift is :-

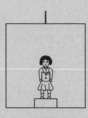

A   stationary

B   moving up at constant speed

C   moving down at constant speed

D   accelerating up

E   accelerating down   1

4.

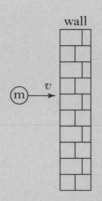

A ball travelling to the right as shown strikes the vertical wall at 90° and rebounds after a perfectly elastic collision with the wall. The change in momentum of the ball is :-

A   zero

B   mv to the left

C   mv to the right

D   2 mv to the left

E   2 mv to the right   1

5. A force is applied to a 2 kg trolley initially at rest on a frictionless horizontal surface. The force-time graph is shown below :-

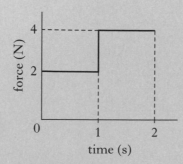

After 2 seconds, the speed of the trolley in ms^{-1} will be :-

A   1·5

B   3·0

C   4·0

D   6·0

E   12   1

6. A golfer hits a golf ball into the wind on an approach shot to the green. The ball leaves the ground with a speed of 20 ms^{-1} at point 1 and follows the path through points 2, 3 and 4 before hitting the ground at point 5. If air resistance can **not** be ignored, which statement about the ball's energy is correct?

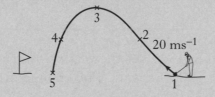

A   Its gravitational potential energy is greatest at point 2.

B   Its gravitational potential energy must equal its kinetic energy when it reaches point 3.

C   It has no kinetic energy at point 3.

D   Its kinetic energy is greatest at point 1.

E   Its kinetic energy is greatest at point 5.

1

7. A pressure of 2 k Pa is produced by :-

   A   A force of 2 N acting on an area of 10 cm^2

   B   A force of 2 N acting on an area of 100 cm^2

   C   A force of 20 N acting on an area of 1000 cm^2

   D   A force of 200 N acting on an area of 1 m^2

   E   A force of 2000 N acting on an area of 10 m^2 **1**

8.

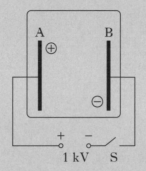

The diagram shows two metal plates inside a vacuum tube. An electron is positioned at plate B and a proton is positioned at plate A. When the switch S is closed, the particles accelerate across to the opposite plates. Which statement correctly describes the particles as they reach the opposite plates?

   A   The proton is travelling faster than the electron.

   B   The proton has more kinetic energy than the electron.

   C   The particles' kinetic energies are equal.

   D   The electron is travelling slower than the proton.

   E   The electron has more kinetic energy than the proton.   **1**

9. All the resistors shown below have the same resistance. Which combination has the biggest resistance between terminals X and Y?

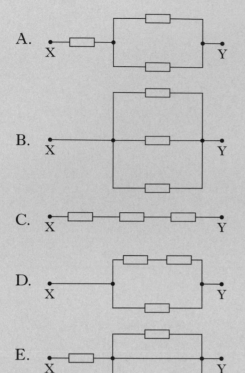

1

10.

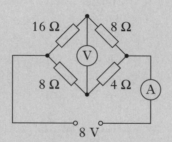

Which row in the table shows the correct values for both meter readings in the above circuit?

	Voltmeter reading (V)	Ammeter reading (A)
A	0	0
B	0	1
C	4	0
D	8	0
E	8	1

1

11. The power dissipated in circuit 1 is 1000 W. What power is dissipated in circuit 2?

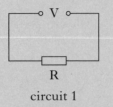

circuit 1

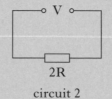

circuit 2

A   250 W

B   500 W

C   1000 W

D   2000 W

E   5000 W

1

12. In the circuit below, the capacitor is charged with the switch at position A, then discharged through variable resistor R by moving the switch to B. The current time graph for the discharge is shown below :-

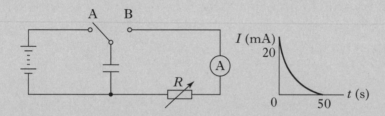

1

The capacitor is charged again, then the value of the variable resistor is reduced. The new discharge graph could be :-

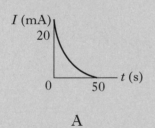

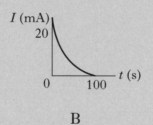

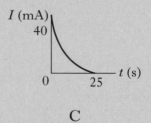

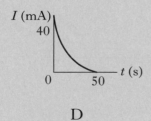

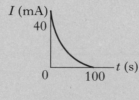

13.

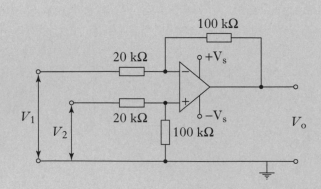

In the circuit above, the output voltage V_o is -5 V. If the 20 kΩ resistors exchange places with the 100 kΩ resistors the output voltage will be :-

A   +5 V

B   −25 V

C   −5 V

D   −1 V

E   −0·2 V   1

14. The diagrams show rays of light inside three transparent blocks with refractive indices shown. The rays hit the edges of the blocks at 42°. In which block(s) will total internal reflection occur?

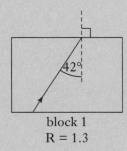

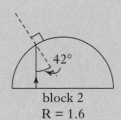

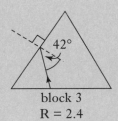

block 1   block 2   block 3
R = 1.3   R = 1.6   R = 2.4

A   Block 1 only

B   Block 3 only

C   Blocks 1 and 2

D   Blocks 2 and 3

E   All of the blocks   1

15. Waves from two coherent sources S_1 and S_2 produce an interference pattern on a screen as shown. If distances $S_1 x = 25 \cdot 62$ cm and $S_2 x = 27 \cdot 22$ cm the wavelength of the waves is :-

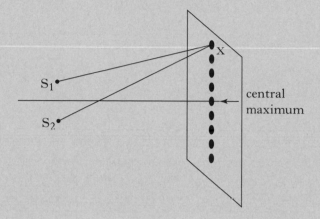

A $0 \cdot 32$ cm

B $0 \cdot 40$ cm

C $0 \cdot 64$ cm

D $0 \cdot 80$ cm

E $1 \cdot 60$ cm   1

16. A photon is emitted from an infra red source when an electron makes the transition shown below.

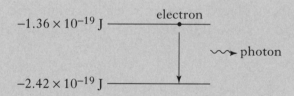

A pulse of infra red radiation from the source has an energy of 25 J. How many photons are in the pulse?

A $1 \cdot 84 \times 10^{20}$

B $1 \cdot 03 \times 10^{20}$

C $2 \cdot 36 \times 10^{20}$

D $2 \cdot 65 \times 10^{-18}$

E $4 \cdot 24 \times 10^{-21}$

1

17. A lamp which can be treated as a point source illuminates the pages of a book 1 metre away with an irradiance I. If the book is moved to a distance 2 metres from the lamp the irradiance will be :-

A $\dfrac{I}{\sqrt{2}}$

B $\sqrt{2}\,I$

C $\dfrac{I}{2}$

D $\dfrac{I}{4}$

E 2I

1

18. A gamma source with a half life of 50 hours is placed beside the detector which registers an activity of 1000 Bq.

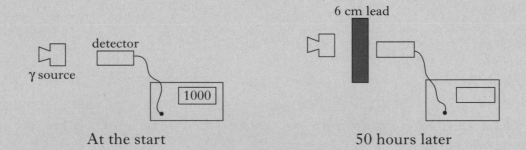

At the start   50 hours later

A piece of lead, 6 cm thick, is placed between the source and the counter. The half value thickness of lead is 3 cm. The reading on the counter after 50 hours will be:

A 1000 Bq

B 500 Bq

C 250 Bq

D 125 Bq

E 62·5 Bq

1

19. Radiation of different frequencies is directed at a clean zinc plate in a vacuum tube as shown below :-

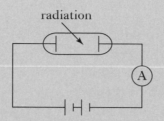

Which graph shows the relationship between current and frequency?

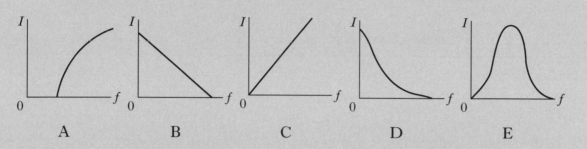

| A | B | C | D | E | 1 |

20. The radioactive nuclide Thorium 232 decays into one of its isotopes, Thorium 228. This process involves the emission of a total of :-

A   one α particle

B   one β particle

C   two α particles and one β particle

D   two β particles and one α particle

E   two α particles and two β particles   1

PART 2

C1. A pupil constructs a homemade pinball machine to demonstrate some physics principles for a school open day.

She tests two springs, A and B, in the launcher and manages to compress the springs fully by 0·1 metres as shown in the graph.

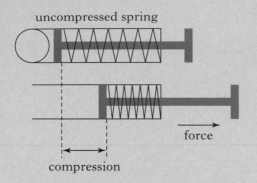

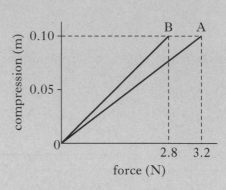

(*a*) If the area under the force/distance graph is a measure of the elastic potential energy stored in the spring, explain why spring A should be able to launch a ball at greater speed than spring B.　　　　2

(*b*) (i) If the elastic potential energy in spring A was transferred to a 20 g ballbearing, show that the ballbearing could be launched at a speed of 4 ms⁻¹.　　　　2

(ii) Explain why, in practice, the launch speed would be less than 4 ms⁻¹.

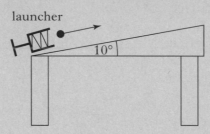

　　　　1

(*c*) She constructs the pinball table with a 10° slope, and launches a ballbearing up the slope at an initial speed of 2·8 ms⁻¹.

Calculate the acceleration of the ballbearing on the slope after leaving the spring launcher (friction on the slope can be ignored).　　　　2

(*d*) Calculate how far up the slope the ball would travel before coming to rest.　　　　2

C2. The velocity/time graph below records data from an experiment to determine the percentage of kinetic energy lost when a 45g golf ball bounces off the ground.

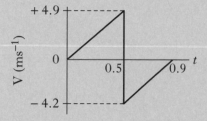

(a) Calculate the change in momentum of the ball as a result of the bounce. **2**

(b) The time of contact with the ground was 2ms. Calculate the resultant force on the golf ball. **2**

(c) Show by calculation that the golf ball loses just over 25% of its kinetic energy as a result of this bounce. **3**

(d) A student performing the experiment produces the results listed below. Use the results to calculate an appropriate value for the percentage of energy lost and its uncertainty.

% E_k lost in bounce	26·5	24·0	29·2	28·8	24·0
	24·2	25·1	24·4	28·9	27·9

2

C3.

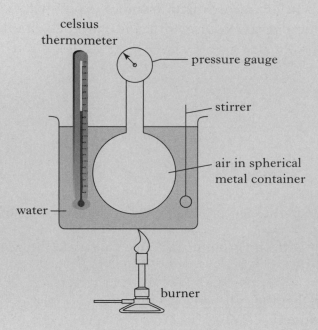

The apparatus shown in the diagram is used to find the relationship between the pressure of a fixed mass of gas and its temperature. One pupil heats the water in the beaker quickly to reduce any heat loss and removes the metal stirrer because it may absorb some of the heat.

A second pupil uses the same apparatus later on, heating slowly and stirring regularly.

(a) State which method you prefer, giving one reason to justify your choice. **1**

(b) A set of data is obtained from the apparatus as shown in the table :-

T (°c)	21	40	59	81	100
P (kPa)	100·0	106·8	113·7	120·5	127·3

Use all of the data to show the relationship between the volume and the temperature of the air in the container. **3**

(c) Explain the increase in the pressure with increasing temperature in this experiment by referring to the kinetic model of gases. **2**

C4. Scientists investigating the nature of matter with the new proton collider at CERN in Geneva accelerate protons close to the speed of light using a series of different devices. The diagram below is a simple sketch. of a linear acceleration which begins the process :-

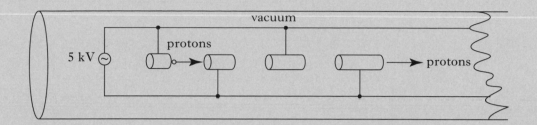

Protons are accelerated, passing through one hollow tube to the next, gaining kinetic energy from each pulse by a series of 5 kV voltage pulses.

(a) (Using data in the data sheet,) show that a stationary proton would reach a speed of $9 \cdot 8 \times 10^5 \, \text{ms}^{-1}$ after the first 5 kV pulse.   **2**

(b) When the acceleration is running at high power, a beam consisting of 10^{11} protons can pass through one of the tubes in $0 \cdot 1 \, \mu\text{s}$. Show by calculation that the proton beam current is 160 mA.   **2**

C5. A student is given a power supply with an emf of 12 volts and an internal resistance of 2 Ω and two heating elements of resistances 1 Ω and 2 Ω. He is asked to choose the element which will provide more power to heat the water as quickly as possible and to prove his choice is correct with the help of ammeter and voltmeter readings.

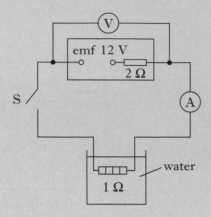

He chooses the 1 Ω element. He argues that the lower resistance will result in a larger current and this in turn will produce more power.

(a) With switch S closed, calculate the readings on

   (i)   the ammeter

   (ii)   the voltmeter   1

(b) Use your readings in (a) to show that the power delivered to the heating element is 16 W.   1

(c) Calculate the heating power available if the 2 Ω resistor is used in the circuit and state whether the student was correct in his choice.   4

C6.

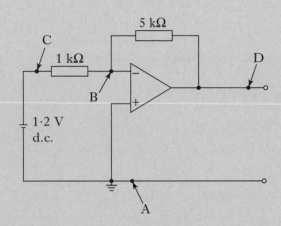

The circuit shows an operational amplifier connected to a 1·2 volt d.c. supply.

(a) In what mode is the amplifier operating?   **1**

(b) Find the potentials at the following points in the circuit:-

    (i) A

    (ii) B

    (iii) C

    (iv) D   **3**

(c) The d.c. supply is replaced by an a.c. supply and the 5kΩ feedback resistor is replaced by a resistor of greater value.

The input and output voltages are shown below :-

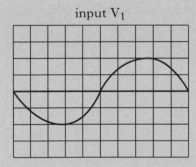

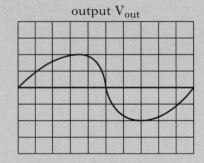

    input V_1 output V_{out}

Y gain 0·1 V per division   Y gain 5 V per division

Timebase 1 ms per division   Timebase 1 ms per division

Calculate   (i)   the gain   **2**

           (ii)   the value of the new feedback resistor   **1**

           (iii)   the frequency of the a.c. signal   **2**

C7. The circuit below is used to draw a graph of voltage against current for a light emitting diode (LED) :-

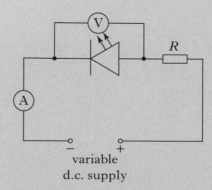

variable
d.c. supply

(a) Explain how the movement of charge carriers causes the production of light at the p n junction of the LED.　　　　**1**

(b) The voltage is gradually increased from zero to a maximum of 6 V and the graph below is obtained.

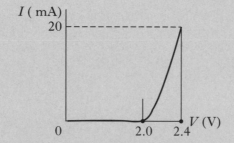

Calculate the value of resistor R.　　　　**2**

(c) The LED begins to light with a voltage of 2·0 V across it. Calculate the frequency of light emitted by the LED.　　　　**3**

(d) Calculate the wavelength of the light from the LED and state whether this is a red or a blue LED.　　　　**1**

C8. Two microwave transmitters are connected to a power supply and act as coherent sources. The transmitters are stated to operate on a frequency of 5×10^9 Hz $\pm$ 10%.

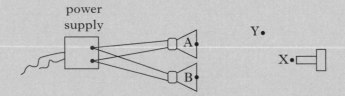

A pupil is asked to use a microwave probe and make some measurements to check the accuracy of the transmitter frequency. He positions the probe at X and detects a well defined maximum signal. He finds the next maximum at Y. Careful measurements with a metre stick yield the following results:

AX = 95·0 cm   BX = 95·0 cm   AY = 89·2 cm   BY = 95·0 cm

(a) Which wave property is responsible for the signals at X and Y?   1

(b) Calculate the value for the wavelength of the microwaves.   2

(c) From this result, state whether the quoted frequency is acceptable.   2
    Explain your answer

C9. A radioactive source emits gamma rays of frequency $1 \cdot 6 \times 10^{20}$ Hz.

(a) Calculate the energy of a gamma photon emitted by the source.   2

(b) The source has an activity of 50 kBq. A scientist is exposed to the source for one hour and he absorbs 20% of the radiation from the source.

  (i)   How many gamma photons are absorbed in the hour?   2

  (ii) The radiation weighting factor of this source is $0 \cdot 9$. Calculate the equivalent dose absorbed by the scientist if his mass is 60 kg.   2

(c) Compare this value to the annual effective dose received by a person in the UK due to natural sources and state whether you think the scientist has been placed in significant danger.   1

C10. A nuclear worker performs a test on a metal that will be used to construct boxes to transport radioactive material.

Different thicknesses of the metal are placed between a detector and the source as shown.

Radioactive source   metal   Geiger-Muller tube

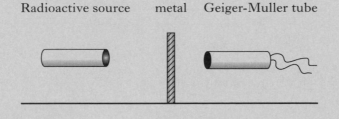

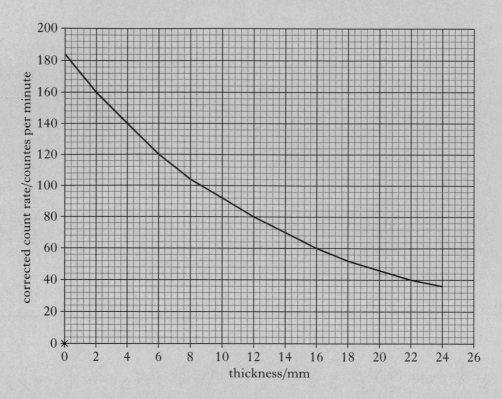

(a) (i) Determine the half-value thickness of the metal. **1**

(ii) A sample of the radioactive material to be transported has a dose equivalent rate of $40\mu Svh^{-1}$ close to the sample. If an acceptable dose equivalent rate close to the sample during transportation in the box is $5\mu Svh^{-1}$ determine a suitable thickness for the walls of the metal box. **2**

(b) The statement below represents a fission reaction:

$$^{235}_{92}u + ^{1}_{0}n \rightarrow ^{134}_{52}Te + X + 4\,^{1}_{0}n$$

(i) State and explain whether the fission reaction is spontaneous or induced. **1**

(ii) Use the SQA Data book to identify the 'unknown' element represented by the letter X. **1**

(iii) Using the information in the table, calculate the energy released in the reaction.

	Mass/kg
$^{235}_{92}u$	$3\cdot901 \times 10^{-25}$
$^{134}_{52}Te$	$2\cdot221 \times 10^{-25}$
X	$1\cdot626 \times 10^{-25}$
$^{1}_{0}n$	$0\cdot017 \times 10^{-25}$

3

[End of Question Paper]

Worked Answers

1. A
- All other quantities are vectors.

2. B
- The velocity/time graph is a *straight* line. This means that the acceleration is uniform. If the gradient of the v/t graph does not change then the acceleration does not change.

3. D
- $s = vt$
$\Rightarrow$ Range, $x = 200 \times t$

- To find t, use $s = \frac{1}{2}at^2$

$$78 \cdot 4 = \frac{1}{2} \times 9 \cdot 8 \times t^2$$

$$\Rightarrow t = 4s$$

4. A
- The forces are

$$\text{mg sin } \theta \text{ (49 N)} \quad \text{friction} \quad 69 \text{ N}$$

- The *resultant force F* can be found in 2 ways:
$F = ma = 10 \times 1 = 10N$
AND $F = 69 - 49 -$ friction

Put the two equations together:
$10 = 69 - 49 -$ friction $\Rightarrow$ friction $= 10N$

5. D
- Change of momentum (or impulse) = Area under an F/t graph

6. B
- Kinetic energy changes to potential energy.

- $\frac{1}{2}mv^2 = mgh$
$$\Rightarrow v^2 = 2gh \Rightarrow h = \frac{v^2}{2g}$$
$$= \frac{4}{2 \times 9 \cdot 8} = 0 \cdot 2m$$

7. D
- $\frac{PV}{T} = $ a constant

$$\frac{P_1 \times 2}{T_1} = \frac{2P_1 \times V}{2T_1}$$

$$\Rightarrow V = 2m^3$$

8. D
- Molecular spacing in a gas is approximately 10 times larger than in a liquid so volumes of gases are $10 \times 10 \times 10 = 1000$ larger than the equivalent mass of liquid.

9. B
- $qV = \frac{1}{2}mv^2$

- If V is made 4 times larger then kinetic energy will become 4 times larger.

The mass does not change so the speed must be 2 times larger.

10. C
- Sort out voltages first:

$$V \qquad 2 V$$

- Now sort out resistances:

$$R \qquad 2 R$$

$$\frac{R}{2}$$

- Now use $I = \frac{V}{R}$ to show that

A_2 reads $\frac{2V}{R}$ and A_3 reads

$$\frac{V}{\frac{1}{2}R} = \frac{2V}{R}$$

11. C

$$I = \frac{T_p d}{external\,R} = \frac{1 \cdot 2}{2}$$
$$= 0 \cdot 6\,A$$

12. E

- In this a.c. capacitor circuit $I \propto f$.

13. D

- With time base off, a.c. voltages appear as a vertical line

- d.c. voltages appear as a dot

- Now use the y gain (volts per division) setting to get $V_{peak} = 2 \times 5 = 10V$

14. E

- This is about *saturation*.

- The op. amp will produce a square wave if the gain formula predicts an output voltage much bigger than the supply voltage (12v).

- The only gain value big enough here is where $\frac{R_f}{R_1} = \frac{20}{1}$

15. C

- Angle of incidence = Angle of reflection.

- The angles of a triangle add up to 180°

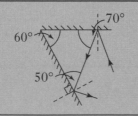

16. E

- Refractive Index $= \dfrac{\sin \theta_{air}}{\sin \theta_{glass}}$

$\theta_{air} = 55°$ $\qquad$ $\theta_{glass} = 33°$

17. A

- $\lambda = d \sin \theta$

$\sin \theta = \dfrac{\lambda}{d}$

To increase θ, λ must be increased (or f decreased) or d reduced.

18. A

- $E = hf$ $\qquad$ $v = f\lambda$

- The longest λ is the smallest f; this results from the transition which releases a photon with the smallest energy.

19. D

- Inverse square law.

- If the distance is increased 3 times then irradiance is reduced 9 times.

- OR Use the formula: $Id^2 = $ constant
$I_1 d_1^2 = I_2 d_2^2 \Rightarrow 36 \times 2^2 = I_2 \times 6^2$

$\Rightarrow I_2 = \dfrac{36 \times 2^2}{6^2} = 4$

20. C

- Learn it!

A1. This question requires equations of motion:

$$v^2 = u^2 + 2as, \; s = ut + \frac{1}{2}at^2, \; \bar{v} = \frac{s}{t}$$

(a) Runner A $\quad u = 0$

$\qquad a = 1\cdot6 \qquad\qquad s = \frac{1}{2}at^2 \Rightarrow t^2 = \frac{2s}{a} \Rightarrow t = \sqrt{\frac{2s}{a}}$

$\qquad s = 11\cdot2$

$\qquad t = ? \qquad\qquad\qquad t = \sqrt{\frac{22\cdot4}{1\cdot4}} = 3\cdot74\,s$

Runner B $\quad u = 0$

$\qquad a = 1\cdot14 \qquad\qquad t = \sqrt{\frac{22\cdot4}{1\cdot4}} = 4\cdot00\,s$

$\qquad s = 11\cdot2$

$\qquad t = ?$

Total time for A = $3\cdot74 + 0\cdot26 = 4\cdot00$ s

Total time for B = $4\cdot00 + 0\cdot20 = 4\cdot20$ s $\hfill$ (3)

$\Rightarrow$ A is $0\cdot20$ s ahead of B

(b) $v^2 = u^2 + 2as$

$\qquad = 0 + 2 \times 1\cdot4 \times 11\cdot2 \Rightarrow v = 5\cdot6 \text{ ms}^{-1}$ $\hfill$ (2)

OR $\quad v = u + at$

$\qquad = 0 + 1\cdot4 \times 4 \Rightarrow 5\cdot6 \text{ ms}^{-1}$

(c) Time for initial $11\cdot2$ m = $4\cdot20$ s

Time to run remaining $48\cdot8$ m at $5\cdot6$ ms^{-1} $\; t = \frac{s}{v}$

$\Rightarrow t = \frac{48\cdot8}{5\cdot6} = 8\cdot71\,s$

$\Rightarrow$ Total time = $8\cdot71 + 4\cdot20 = 12\cdot91$ s $\hfill$ (2)

A2. Remember both Newton's 1st and 2nd Laws in this question. You also require the idea of resolving a vector into two components.

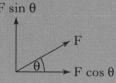

And remember upthrust depends on pressure difference. Pressure depends on "depth" in a fluid.

(a) Weight = mg = $600 \times 9\cdot8 = 5880$ N $\hfill$ (2)

(b) Upthrust results from the fact that pressure in a fluid such as air is proportional to depth. Thus, the pressure (upwards) on the bottom of the balloon is less than the pressure (downwards) on the top of the balloon. Force = Pressure × Area so there is resultant upwards force due to the fluid. $\hfill$ (2)

(c) The balloon is stationary therefore the resultant force on it is zero.

$T + mg - U = 0$

$T = U - mg = 6180 - 5880$ (2)

$\Rightarrow T = 300$ N

(d) $a = \dfrac{F}{m} = \dfrac{6180 - 5880}{600} = 0 \cdot 5\,\text{ms}^{-2}$ (2)

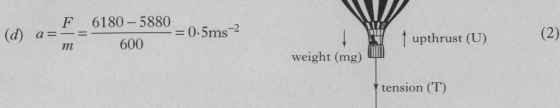

(e)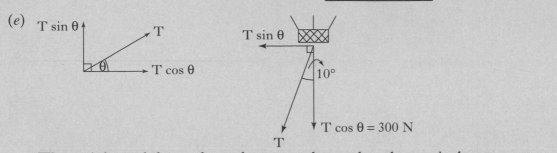

The weight and the upthrust have not changed so the vertical component of the tension still has to provide 300 N otherwise the balloon would be subject to a resultant force in the vertical direction.

$T \cos \theta = 300 \Rightarrow T \cos 10° = 300$

$$\Rightarrow T = \frac{300}{\cos 10°} \Rightarrow T = 304 \cdot 6\,\text{N}$$ (2)

A3. Remember W = mg; $P = \dfrac{F}{A}$; P = ρgh for this question and don't forget Newton's 1st Law.

(a) The container is not accelerating; the resultant force on it is therefore zero.

$\Rightarrow$ Upthrust = 0·49 N   (1)

(b) $P = \dfrac{F}{A} = \dfrac{0 \cdot 49}{5 \times 10^{-4}} = 980\,\text{Pa}$ (2)

(c) $P = ρgh \Rightarrow ρ = \dfrac{P}{gh} = \dfrac{980}{9 \cdot 8 \times 0 \cdot 1}$

$\Rightarrow ρ = 1000\,\text{kg m}^{-3}$ (2)

(d) The weight and area of the container are unchanged therefore the pressure $\frac{F}{A}$ is unchanged. This means that ρgh can not have changed.

If ρ is doubled then h must be halved

$\Rightarrow$ depth = 5 cm (1)

A4. Remember P = VI   V = IR

$\left(or\ P = \dfrac{V^2}{R}\right)$ and $\dfrac{1}{R_T} = \dfrac{1}{r_1} + \dfrac{1}{r_2}$

The potential divider formula can also be useful:

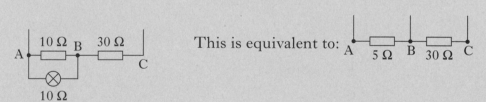

$V_2 = \dfrac{R_2}{(R_1 + R_2)} \cdot V$

(a) $I = \dfrac{P}{V} = \dfrac{0\cdot9}{3} = 0\cdot3A$

$R = \dfrac{V}{I} = \dfrac{3}{0\cdot3} = 10\ \Omega$ OR $P = \dfrac{V^2}{R} \Rightarrow R = \dfrac{V^2}{P} = \dfrac{9}{0\cdot9} = 10\ \Omega$ (2)

(b) BC is the correct position.

The voltage across BC is $\left(\dfrac{10}{10 + 30}\right) \times 12 = 3V$ (2)

(c) Before the bulb is connected, the voltage across AB will be 3V as required. BUT when the 10Ω bulb is connected the new circuit becomes:

This is equivalent to:

Thus the voltage across AB would drop below 3V (approx to 1·7V) and the bulb would be dim. (2)

A5. When the internal resistance equation E = V + Ir is rearranged to V = − rI + E the equation is now of the form $y = mx + c$.

This means the gradient of a graph is equal to − r (the internal resistance), and the intercept on the y axis gives the voltage when the current is zero (i.e. the emf). Short circuit current means current with no external resistance.

(a) $E = V_{tpd} + V_{lost}$

$\Rightarrow E = V_{tpd} + Ir$

$\Rightarrow V_{tpd}\ E - Ir$ (1)

$\Rightarrow V_{tpd} = -rI + E$

(b) V (V)

     emf = 1·4 V

       $r = 1\Omega$

     $\left(grad = \dfrac{y_2 - y_1}{x_2 - x_1} \right)$ (4)

(c)   Short circuit current $I = \dfrac{Emf}{Int.\ res} = \dfrac{1\cdot4}{1} = 1\cdot4$ A   (2)

A6. Know your current/time and voltage/time graphs for charge and discharge of a capacitor. Recall that time of charge or discharge depends on the sizes of both R and C.

(a)   Initial current $I = \dfrac{V}{R} \Rightarrow R_1 = \dfrac{V}{I} = \dfrac{10}{0\cdot02} = 500\Omega$ (2)

(b)   (i)   Shorter time of discharge.   (2)

       (ii)   Larger initial discharge current.

(c) $Q = CV = 20,000 \times 10^{-6} \times 10$

$= 200,000 \times 10^{-6}$ (2)

$= 0\cdot2$ C

(d)   Average $I = \dfrac{Q}{t} = \dfrac{0\cdot2}{25} = 0\cdot008$ A $= 8$mA   (2)

A7. Remember the two modes for an op. amp:

     inverting – one input voltage and differential – 2 input voltages

Gain $= \dfrac{R_f}{R_1}$ $V_{out} = V_2 - V_1\left(\dfrac{R_f}{R_1}\right)$

Memorise the mosfet parts.

(a)   Differential mode.   (1)

(b)   Gain $= \dfrac{R_f}{R_1} = \dfrac{10k}{1k} = 10$ (1)

(c) From the oscilloscope screens:

$$V_1 = 4 \times 0{\cdot}5 = 2V$$

$$V_{out} = 12{\cdot}58 \times 5{\cdot}0 = 9V$$

$$V_{out} = (V_2 - V_1)\left(\frac{R_f}{R_1}\right)$$

$$\Rightarrow 9 = (V_2 - 2)\left(\frac{10}{1}\right)$$

$$\Rightarrow 9 = 10V_2 - 20$$

$$\Rightarrow 10V_2 = 29 \Rightarrow V_2 = 2{\cdot}9V \tag{3}$$

(d) Mosfet

    A–Source   B–gate   C–drain   (2)

A8. $\dfrac{Sin\,\theta_{air}}{Sin\,\theta_{glass}} = n$

$$Sin\,C = \frac{1}{n}$$

(a) (i) $\dfrac{Sin\,\theta_{air}}{Sin\,\theta_{glass}} = \dfrac{Sin\,31°}{Sin\,20°}$

$$= 1{\cdot}51$$

   (ii) $Sin\,C = \dfrac{1}{n} = \dfrac{1}{1{\cdot}51} \Rightarrow C = 41{\cdot}5°$

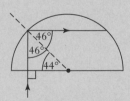

(total internal reflection)

A9. Grating spacing $d = \dfrac{1}{N}$

Grating formula $n\lambda = d\,\sin\theta$,

$\sin\theta = \dfrac{opposite}{hypotenuse}$ $1nm = 10^{-9}m$

Longer wavelengths diffract more than shorter ones. Quote the mean when you have a number of measurements of the same quantity and remember:

$$Random\ uncertainty = \frac{Max - Min}{number\ of\ readings}$$

(a) $n\lambda = d\sin\theta$ $(n = 1)$

$$d = \frac{1}{300}\text{ mm} = \frac{10^{-3}}{300}\text{ m} \qquad \sin\theta = \frac{30}{200}$$

$$\Rightarrow \lambda = \frac{10^{-3}}{300} \times \frac{30}{200} = 5 \times 10^{-7}\text{ m} = 500\text{ nm} \tag{3}$$

(b) Value quoted is the mean $= 502$ nm

$$\text{Random uncertainty} = \frac{511 - 490}{7} = 3$$

Quoted value is 502 ± 3 (2)

A10. Remember the "photoelectric" equations, $E = hf$; $hf = W + E_k$ and don't forget $v = f\lambda$. You also need to understand the idea of "stopping potential" Vs where
$$qV_s = \frac{1}{2}mv^2$$

(a) The photoelectric effect (or photoelectric emission). (1)

(b) $E = hf = \dfrac{hv}{\lambda} = \dfrac{6\cdot63 \times 10^{34} \times 3 \times 10^{8}}{300 \times 10^{-9}} = 6\cdot63 \times 10^{-19}\text{J}$ (2)

(c) $hf = W + E_k$

$6\cdot63 \times 10^{-19} = 4\cdot23 \times 10^{-19} + E_k$ (2)

$\Rightarrow E_k = 2\cdot40 \times 10^{-19}\text{J}$

(d) The photoelectrons still have enough (kinetic) energy to overcome the opposing effect of the electric field. (1)

(e) $qV_s = E_k \Rightarrow V_s = \dfrac{E_k}{q} = \dfrac{2\cdot40 \times 10^{-19}}{1\cdot6 \times 10^{-19}} = 1\cdot5V$ (2)

1.   E

- Uncertainties are:

 ruler $\pm\,0\cdot 5$ mm

 thermometer $\pm\,0\cdot 5$ °C

 stopwatch $\pm\,0\cdot 01$ s

 % uncertainties are:

 $A = \dfrac{0\cdot 01}{1\cdot 00} \times 100 = 1\%$ $B = 0\cdot 1\%$

 $C = 10\%$ $D = 1\cdot 7\%$ $E = 25\%$

2.   E

- The velocity can be found from the gradient of an s/t graph.

 There is a constant gradient

 So the velocity is constant

3.   E

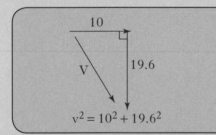

$v^2 = 10^2 + 19\cdot 6^2$

4.   B

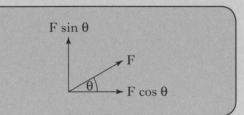

5.   C

- Momentum is conserved.

 Momentum before = Momentum after

 $(2 \times 2) = 4 \times V$

 $\Rightarrow V = 1\,\mathrm{ms^{-1}}$

 Kinetic energy before $= \dfrac{1}{2}\,mv^2$

 $= \dfrac{1}{2} \times 2 \times 2^2$

 $= 4\,\mathrm{J}$

 Kinetic energy after $= \dfrac{1}{2} \times 4 \times 1^2 = 2\,\mathrm{J}$

6.   E

- Potential energy at $X = mgH$

 Potential energy at $Y = mgh$

 Kinetic energy at Y = loss in potential energy

 $= mgH - mgh$

7.   E

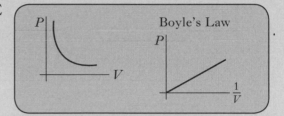

8.   D

- Voltage across R will be 2V. Current is the same in all three resistors. $\dfrac{V}{R}$ is same for all three resistors.

9.   D

- Total power $= I^2\,(R + r)$

 Bulb power $= I^2 R$

 Fraction $\dfrac{I^2 R}{I^2 (R + r)} = \dfrac{R}{(R + r)}$

10.   C

- Capacitance $= \dfrac{\text{Charge}}{\text{Voltage}}$

 Farads $= \dfrac{\text{Coulombs}}{\text{Volts}}$

11.   C

- The graph is a discharge graph.

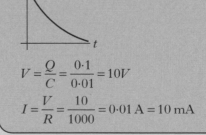

$V = \dfrac{Q}{C} = \dfrac{0\cdot 1}{0\cdot 01} = 10V$

$I = \dfrac{V}{R} = \dfrac{10}{1000} = 0\cdot 01\,\mathrm{A} = 10\,\mathrm{mA}$

12. A

- $f = 100$ Hz

$$T = \frac{1}{100} \text{ s} = \frac{10}{1000} = 10 \text{ ms}$$

4 cm $\equiv$ 10 ms

$\Rightarrow$ Timebase = 2·5 ms per cm

13. D

- $\dfrac{R}{400} = \dfrac{60}{40} \Rightarrow R = 600 \ \Omega$

If R becomes 1200 Ω then:

$$\frac{1200}{400} = \frac{YZ}{(100 - YZ)} \Rightarrow \frac{3}{1} = \frac{YZ}{(100 - YZ)}$$

Solve to get $YZ = 75$ cm.

14. D

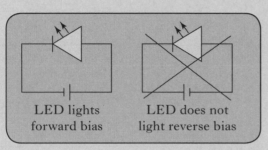

LED lights   LED does not
forward bias   light reverse bias

15. B

- $f = \dfrac{v}{\lambda} = \dfrac{3 \times 10^8}{650 \times 10^{-9}} = 4{\cdot}62 \times 10^{14} \text{Hz}$

Frequency does *not* change in refraction.

$$\frac{\lambda_{\text{air}}}{\lambda_{\text{liquid}}} = 1{\cdot}3 \Rightarrow \lambda_{\text{liquid}} = \frac{650}{1{\cdot}3} \text{ m} = 500 \text{ nm}$$

16. A

- $\lambda = d \sin \theta$

$$\sin \theta = \frac{\lambda}{d}$$

To obtain smallest θ, λ should be smallest and d should be largest, i.e. grating spacing should be smallest value.

17. C

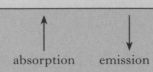

absorption   emission

$E = hf$. A larger energy transition means the photon has higher frequency.

18. D

19. D

- Increasing irradiance means *more photons* are produced. This increases the current (of photoelectrons). The colour (frequency) of this source does not change (E = hf) so individual photoelectrons still have the same energy.

20. C

- 238   234   4

   U $\rightarrow$ Th + He

  92   90   2

B1. Make sure you know your *scalars*: distance, speed, and your *vectors*: displacement, velocity. And remember $\bar{v} = \frac{s}{t}$

(a) A vector has a magnitude (size) and a direction and obeys the laws of vector addition. A scalar has only magnitude and obeys the laws of simple addition. (1)

(b) 6 km bearing 350° (1)

(c) $\bar{v} = \frac{s}{t} = \frac{6}{t}$ bearing 350°

To find t for David we need to get Ben's time then add 5 minutes to it.

Ben's time is $t = \frac{s}{v} = \frac{6}{8} = 0.75$ hour (45 min).

David's time is 50 min or 0·83 hour.

Thus $\bar{v} = \frac{6}{0.83} = 7.2 \ km \ h^{-1}$ bearing 350°. (3)

(d) $\bar{v} = \frac{s}{t}$ $\qquad \frac{6}{1} = 6 \ km \ h^{-1}$ bearing 170°. (1)

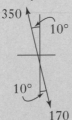

B2. Remember the slope equation

$a = g \sin \theta$ (or $F = mg \sin \theta$).

You also need $v = u + at$ and the resolution of a vector into components.

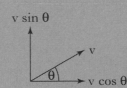

The final part (d) requires $s = ut + \frac{1}{2}at^2$.

(a) $a = g \sin \theta = 9{\cdot}8 \times \sin 30 = 9{\cdot}8 \times 0{\cdot}5 = 4{\cdot}9 \ \text{ms}^{-2}$ (2)

(b) $v = u + at = 0 + 4{\cdot}9 \times 1 = 4{\cdot}9 \ \text{ms}^{-1}$ (2)

(c)   vertical component $= v \sin \theta$

$= 4{\cdot}9 \times \sin 30°$ (2)

$= 2{\cdot}45 \ \text{ms}^{-1}$

(d) $s = ut + \dfrac{1}{2}at^2$

$= (2{\cdot}45 \times 1{\cdot}2) + \dfrac{1}{2} \times 9{\cdot}8 \times (1{\cdot}2)^2$

$= 2{\cdot}94 + 7{\cdot}06$

$= 10 \ m$ (2)

B3. You need $s = vt$ in part (a) but don't forget this is an "echo" question! Newton's 1st Law comes in to part b and his 2nd Law appears in part d. Don't forget 1 tonne = 1000 kg.

(a) Time for sound to travel down to sub *and back*
$t = 25 \times 5 \ \text{ms} = 125 \ \text{ms} = 0{\cdot}125 \ \text{s}.$
$\Rightarrow$ total distance travelled by sound, $s = vt = 1600 \times 0{\cdot}125 = 200 \ m$
$\Rightarrow$ sub is 100 m below the warship (3)

(b) Submarine has zero resultant force on it
$\Rightarrow$ mg = upthrust
$\Rightarrow$ upthrust $= 10{,}000 \times 1000 \times 9{\cdot}8 \ \text{N}$
$\qquad\qquad = 9{\cdot}8 \times 10^7 \ \text{N}$ (2)

(c) Pressure increases with depth. Greater upwards pressure on the bottom of the sub results in an upthrust. (1)

(d) Resultant upward force = Upthrust − weight
$= 9{\cdot}8 \times 10^7 - (9800 \times 1000 \times 9{\cdot}8)$
$= 9{\cdot}8 \times 10^7 - 9{\cdot}6 \times 10^7$
$= 0{\cdot}2 \times 10^7 = 2 \times 10^6 \ \text{N}$ (2)

B4. This question is on momentum conservation.

Remember, momentum is a VECTOR

And $F = \dfrac{\Delta \ mv}{t}$

Don't forget Newtons Third Law.

(a) $(m_1u_1) + (m_2u_2) = MV$

$(1500 \times 10) - (1000 \times 7 \cdot 5) = 2500V$

$\Rightarrow 15000 - 7500 = 2500V$

$\Rightarrow V = \dfrac{15000 - 7500}{2500} = 3 \text{ ms}^{-1}$ (to the right) (2)

(b) Change of momentum = final momentum – initial momentum

$$= 1000 \times 3 - (-1000 \times 7 \cdot 5)$$

$$= 3000 + 7500$$

$$= 10{,}500 \text{ kgms}^{-1} \text{ (to the right)} \tag{2}$$

(c) $F = \dfrac{\Delta mv}{t} = \dfrac{10{,}500}{2} = 5{,}250 \text{N}$ (1)

(d) An equal and opposite force – Newtons Third Law

ie 5,250 to the left (or $- 5{,}250$ N) (2)

B5. If a cell has internal resistance, its emf can be measured using a voltmeter when *no current* is drawn.

BUT, when current flows, the Emf = tpd + lost volts and a voltmeter will read the cell's tpd.

(a) V_2 = the cell emf = 1·5 V (1)

(b) (i) S open, V_1 = the cell emf = 1·5 V. (1)

(ii) S closed, V_1 = tpd:

E = tpd + lost volts
$1 \cdot 5 = IR + Ir$
$1 \cdot 5 = I (9 + 1)$
$\Rightarrow I = 0 \cdot 15$ A $\Rightarrow$ tpd = 1·35 V (2)
$\Rightarrow V_1 = 1 \cdot 35$ V

(c) (i) Mosfet (1)

(ii) $V_{out} = \dfrac{R_f}{R_1} \times (V_2 - V_1)$

$$= \dfrac{20}{1} \times (1 \cdot 5 - 1 \cdot 35)$$

$$= 20 \times 0 \cdot 15 = 3V \tag{2}$$

This voltage exceeds the 2V necessary to switch on the mosfet, thus the alarm will trigger.

B6. This is a tricky question which requires you to understand how the switches S_1 and S_2 control the discharging of the capacitor. You also need to remember the shape of the discharge V/t graph and how the size of the resistor affects the time for discharge. Finally, you will need to be familiar with the idea of oscilloscope timebase.

(a) **AB** Switches S_1 and S_2 are on. Capacitor C has been fully charged. The computer is reading the voltage across both C and R (they are in parallel). This voltage is constant. (1)

BC S_1 is open (off). The battery is no longer connected to the capacitor. It discharges through R. The voltage drops. (1)

CD S_2 is open. There is no current in R. The voltage across R is zero. (1)

(b) The capacitor is discharging too quickly, before the ballbearing can break S_2 and switch off the circuit. He should increase R to slow the discharge.

(2)

(c) The time is 3×50 ms $= 150$ ms. (1)

B7. Practice reading voltages and finding frequencies on oscilloscopes will be necessary here. And you need to be familiar with the effects of frequency on capacitors in a.c. circuits.

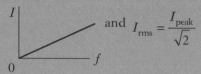

and $I_{rms} = \dfrac{I_{peak}}{\sqrt{2}}$

(a) (i) $V_P = 2 \times 2 = 4V$ (1)

(ii) $f = \dfrac{1}{T}$

$T = 5 \times 0.5$ ms $= 2.5$ ms $= \dfrac{2.5}{1000} s$

$\Rightarrow f = \dfrac{1000}{2.5} = 400\,\text{Hz}$ (2)

(b) $I_p = \dfrac{V_p}{R} = \dfrac{4}{100} = 0.04\,\text{A}$

$I_{rms} = \dfrac{I_p}{\sqrt{2}} = \dfrac{0.04}{\sqrt{2}} = 0.028\ A$ (2)

(c) **A_1** No change because the current in a resistor is not affected by frequency. (1)

A_2 The current in the capacitor will double as current varies directly with frequency in an a.c. capacitive circuit. (2)

B8. $\dfrac{\sin \theta_{\text{air}}}{\sin \theta_{\text{glass}}} = n$

The refractive index, n, varies slightly with frequency (colour) of light.

$v = f\lambda$ and $\sin c = \dfrac{1}{n}$

Don't forget red light has longest wavelength and the lowest frequency of the visible spectrum.

(a) (i) $\lambda_{\text{air}} = \dfrac{v}{f} = \dfrac{3 \times 10^8}{4 \cdot 3 \times 10^{14}} = 7 \cdot 0 \times 10^{-7}\, m$ (2)

(ii) $\dfrac{\lambda_{\text{air}}}{\lambda_{\text{glass}}} = n \quad \Rightarrow \lambda_{\text{glass}} = \dfrac{\lambda_{\text{air}}}{n}$

$$= \dfrac{7 \cdot 0 \times 10^{-7}}{1 \cdot 94} = 3 \cdot 6 \times 10^{-7}\, m$$ (2)

(b) (i)

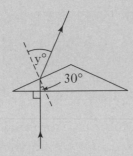

For red light,

$\sin c = \dfrac{1}{n} = \dfrac{1}{1 \cdot 94} \Rightarrow c = 31°$

$\theta_{\text{glass}} = 30°$. The critical angle is not exceeded so the red beam will be refracted as shown.

For violet light

$\sin c = \dfrac{1}{n} = \dfrac{1}{2 \cdot 06} \Rightarrow c = 29°$

The critical angle is exceeded so total internal reflection will occur as shown. (3)

(ii) $\dfrac{\sin \theta_{\text{air}}}{\sin \theta_{\text{glass}}} = 1 \cdot 94$

$\Rightarrow \sin \theta_{\text{air}} = 1 \cdot 94 \times \sin \theta_{\text{glass}} = 1 \cdot 94 \sin 30°$ (2)
$\Rightarrow \theta_{\text{air}} = 75 \cdot 9°$
$\Rightarrow y = 75 \cdot 9°$

For reflection $i = r \Rightarrow z = 30°$

B9. Equations needed here are:

$\lambda = \dfrac{v}{f}, \qquad n\lambda = d \sin \theta \qquad d = \dfrac{1}{N}$

(a) An electron receiving a quantum of energy can be raised to an excited state. An incoming photon which happens to have exactly the same quantum of energy can induce or "stimulate" the electron to fall back down to the lower state and emit a photon identical in energy, phase and direction to the incoming photon. (2)

(b) (i) $d = \dfrac{1}{N} = \dfrac{1}{600} \times 10^{-3}\, m = 1 \cdot 67 \times 10^{-6}\, m$ (2)

(ii) $\lambda = d \sin \theta$

$\Rightarrow \sin \theta = \dfrac{\lambda}{d}$

For red light $\sin \theta = \dfrac{6 \cdot 25 \times 10^{-7}}{1 \cdot 67 \times 10^{-6}} \Rightarrow \theta = 22 \cdot 0°$

For green light $\sin \theta = \dfrac{5 \cdot 00 \times 10^{-7}}{1 \cdot 67 \times 10^{-6}} \Rightarrow \theta = 17 \cdot 4°$ (3)

The red light subtends the bigger angle. So the dot at y is red.

B10. Make sure you can distinguish between fusion and fission and remember the equation $E = mc^2$ is used in both processes.

(a) Nuclear fusion occurs when two nuclei of lower mass numbers combine to form a nucleus of larger mass number. Some mass is destroyed in the process and transforms to energy ($E = mc^2$). (1)

(b)
Mass before fusion	Mass after fusion
3·342	6·642
+ 5·005	+ 1·674
$8 \cdot 347 \times 10^{-27}$ kg	$8 \cdot 316 \times 10^{-27}$ kg

$m = 8 \cdot 347 - 8 \cdot 316 \times 10^{-27}$
$\quad = 0 \cdot 031 \times 10^{-27}$ kg
$E = mc^2 = 0 \cdot 031 \times 10^{-27} \times 9 \times 10^{16} = 2 \cdot 79 \times 10^{-12}$ J (3)

(c) Energy required from one pulse $= 100 \times 1 \cdot 5 \times 10^6$
$= 1 \cdot 5 \times 10^8$ J
Energy from one fusion $= 2 \cdot 79 \times 10^{-12}$ J

$\Rightarrow$ Number of fusions required $= \dfrac{1 \cdot 5 \times 10^8}{2 \cdot 79 \times 10^{-12}} = 5 \cdot 38 \times 10^{19}$ (2)

1. E

• The newton is the unit of force. Which of these quantities could be equal to force?

   A $F = Et$　　　　　No

   B $F = mvt$　　　　No

   C $F = Es$　　　　　No

   D $F = mvd$　　　　No

   E $F = \dfrac{E}{s}$ $(E = Fs)$ YES.

2. D

• Uniform acceleration

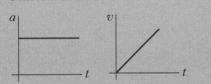

3. D

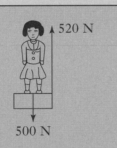

Unbalanced force 20N upwards will produce an acceleration upwards.

4. D

• Momentum is a *vector*

Change of momentum
= final momentum − initial momentum

$\longleftarrow$　　　　　$\longrightarrow$

  $(-mv)$　　　　　$(+mv)$

   $= (-mv) - (+mv) = -2mv$

5. B

• Impulse = Change of momentum
      = area under F/t graph

Change of momentum = 2 + 4 = 6 kg ms^{-1}

$mv = 6 \Rightarrow v = 3$ ms^{-1}

6. D

7. A

• $P = \dfrac{F \text{ in newtons}}{A \text{ in m}^2}$

$1 \text{m}^2 = 10{,}000 \text{ cm}^2$

$1 \text{k Pa} = 1000 \text{ Pa}.$

8. C

• $qV = \dfrac{1}{2} mv^2$

Both particles have the same size of charge q and are accelerated by the same voltage V.

9. C

• Remember $R_T = r_1 + r_2$ for series

$\dfrac{1}{R_T} = \dfrac{1}{r_1} + \dfrac{1}{r_2}$ for parallel

In a parallel arrangement the total resistance is always smaller than the smallest resistor.

10. B

• Balanced Wheatstone Bridge-V reads zero.

$\dfrac{1}{R} = \dfrac{1}{24} + \dfrac{1}{12} \Rightarrow R = 8\Omega$

$\Rightarrow I = 1A$

11. B

• $P = \dfrac{V^2}{R}$

If V is same but R is doubled in circuit 2, then power is halved.

12. C

• $I = \dfrac{V}{R}$. If R is reduced the initial current will be larger. If R is reduced the time will be reduced.

13. E

- (1) $V_{out} = \dfrac{R_f}{R_1}(V_2 - V_1)$

  $-5 = \dfrac{100}{20}(V_2 - V_1)$

  $\Rightarrow (V_2 - V_1) = -1\,V$

- (2) $V_{out} = \dfrac{20}{100}(-1) = -0\cdot2\,V$

14. D

- $\sin c = \dfrac{1}{n}$ Block 1 c = 50·3°

  Block 2 c = 38·7°

  Block 3 c = 24·6°

15. B

- Path difference for 4th

  maximum = 4λ

  $4\lambda = 27\cdot22 - 25\cdot62$

  $= 1\cdot6\,cm$

  $\lambda = 0\cdot4\,cm$

16. C

- Energy of photon $= -1\cdot36 \times 10^{-19}$

  $\qquad\qquad -(-2\cdot42 \times 10^{-19})$

  $= 1\cdot06 \times 10^{-19}\,J$

  Number of photons needed for 25J

  $= \dfrac{25}{1\cdot06 \times 10^{-19}} = 2\cdot36 \times 10^{20}$ photons

17. D

- $Id^2 = $ a constant

  If the new irradiance is I_x then:

  $I \times 1^2 = I_x \times 2^2$

  $I_x = \dfrac{I \times 1^2}{2^2} = \dfrac{I}{4}$

18. D

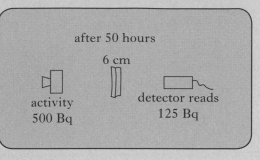

after 50 hours

6 cm

activity
500 Bq

detector reads
125 Bq

19. A

20. D

- $^{232}_{90}\text{Th} \rightarrow {}^{228}_{90}\text{Th} + ?$

  Mass reduction must be due to the emission of one α particle.

  $^{232}_{90}\text{Th} \rightarrow {}^{228}_{90}\text{Th} + {}^{4}_{2}\alpha$

  Now to balance the proton number you need the emission of two β particles

  $^{232}_{90}\text{Th} \rightarrow {}^{228}_{90}\text{Th} + {}^{4}_{2}\alpha + {}^{0}_{-1}\beta + {}^{0}_{-1}\beta$

C1. Remember, Work done = Area under F/s graph.

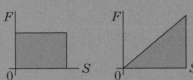

and a useful formula here is, Work, $E_w = \frac{1}{2}mv^2$

You also need to recall the acceleration on slope (angle θ) = $g \sin θ$ and, finally, an equation of motion $v^2 = u^2 + 2as$ will be needed.

(a) The energy stored in the springs when compressed is:

A $\quad \frac{1}{2} \times 3·2 \times 0·1 = 0·16$ J

B $\quad \frac{1}{2} \times 2·8 \times 0·1 = 0·14$ J

Spring A stores more energy and should therefore be able to provide the ball with more kinetic energy. (2)

(b) (i) $E = \frac{1}{2}mv^2$

$$v^2 = \frac{2E}{m} \Rightarrow v = \sqrt{\frac{2E}{m}} = \sqrt{\frac{2 \times 0·16}{0·02}} = 4 ms^{-1}$$ (2)

(ii) Energy would be lost as heat due to frictional forces in the launcher. (1)

(c) $a = g \sin θ = 9·8 \times \sin 10°$
$\qquad\qquad = 9·8 \times 0·174 = 1·7 \text{ ms}^{-2}$ down the slope (2)

(d) v = 0 $\qquad v^2 = u^2 + 2as \qquad \Rightarrow 2as = v^2 - u^2$

u = 2·8

a = −1·7 $\qquad s = \dfrac{v^2 - u^2}{2a} = \dfrac{0 - (2·8)^2}{2 \times -1·7}$
s = ?

$\qquad\qquad\qquad = 2·3 \ m$ (2)

C2. Remember that distance travelled = Area under a speed/time graph.

You will also need the formula $F = \Delta \frac{mv}{t}$

For part d) quote the average and calculate the random uncertainty

$$\frac{\text{Max - Min}}{\text{number of readings}}$$

(a) Change in momentum $= mv - mu$ (Remember momentum is a vector).
$= (0 \cdot 045 \times -4 \cdot 2) - (0 \cdot 045 \times 4 \cdot 9)$
$= -0 \cdot 189 - 0 \cdot 221 = -0 \cdot 410 \text{ kgms}^{-1}$ (2)

(b) $F = \dfrac{mv - mu}{t} = \dfrac{-0 \cdot 410}{0.002} = -205N$ (2)

(c) E_k before bounce $= \dfrac{1}{2} \times 0 \cdot 045 \times (4 \cdot 9)^2 = 0 \cdot 540 \text{ J}$

E_k after bounce $= \dfrac{1}{2} \times 0 \cdot 045 \times (4 \cdot 2)^2 = 0 \cdot 397 \text{ J}$

Loss in $E_k = 0 \cdot 143 \text{ J}$

$\% \text{ loss} = \dfrac{0 \cdot 143}{0 \cdot 540} \times 100 = 26 \cdot 5\%$ (3)

(d) Mean $= \dfrac{2631}{10} = 26 \cdot 3\%$ Random uncertainty $= \dfrac{29 \cdot 2 - 24 \cdot 0}{10} = 0 \cdot 5$ (2)

C3. To verify the relationship between P and T, either: Calculate values of T in Kelvin then show that each of the 5 sets of $\frac{P}{T}$ values is constant.

Or draw a graph of P vs T$_{(kelvin)}$ and produce a straight line through the origin.

This indicates that P $\propto$ T or $\frac{P}{T} = k$.

An understanding of the kinetic model for gases is also important for part d).

(*a*) The second method is preferable. Slow heating allows more time for the air temperature to become the same as the water temperature. The thermometer will then provide a more reliable temperature reading.

OR Stirring will help "even out" any variations in temperature in the water. (1)

(*b*)

T(°C)	21	40	59	82	100
T(K)	294	313	332	355	373
P(kPa)	100·0	106·8	113·7	120·5	127·3

$\dfrac{100}{294} = 0.340 \quad \dfrac{106.8}{313} = 0.341 \quad \dfrac{113.7}{332} = 0.342$

$\dfrac{120.5}{355} = 0.339 \quad \dfrac{127.3}{373} = 0.341$

From the data $\dfrac{P}{T_{(k)}}$ = a constant.

OR, P $\propto$ T$_{(k)}$ (3)

(*c*) Increasing temperature means increasing the average kinetic energy of the molecules.

The molecules have higher speeds, therefore they collide *faster* and also *more often* with the container. The increased force in each collision results in an increased gas pressure. (2)

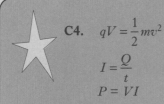

C4. $qV = \frac{1}{2}mv^2$

$I = \frac{Q}{t}$

$P = VI$

and don't forget, protons have the same *size* of charge as electrons $1 \cdot 6 \times 10^{-19}$C.

(a) $qV = \frac{1}{2}mv^2 \Rightarrow v^2 = \frac{2qV}{m} \Rightarrow v = \sqrt{\frac{2qV}{m}}$

$$= \sqrt{\frac{2 \times 1 \cdot 6 \times 10^{-19} \times 5 \times 10^3}{1 \cdot 673 \times 10^{-27}}}$$

$$= 9 \cdot 78 \times 10^5 \ ms^{-1}$$ (2)

(b) $I = \frac{Q}{t} = \frac{10^{11} \times 1 \cdot 6 \times 10^{-19}}{0 \cdot 1 \times 10^{-6}}$

$$= 0 \cdot 16 \ A \ (160 \ mA)$$ (2)

C5. You need the internal resistance formula in this question.

$E_{mf} = V_{tpd} + V_{lost}$

$E = IR + Ir$

and $P = VI$

(a) (i) $I = \frac{E}{(R + r)} = \frac{12}{2 + 1} = 4A$ (1)

(ii) $V_{reads\ tpd} = IR = 4 \times 1 = 4V$

(b) $P = V_{tpd}I = 4 \times 4 = 16 \ W$ (1)

(c) To find P for the new resistor we must find (1)

I and V_{tpd} to get $P = V_{tpd} \ I$.

$I = \frac{12}{4} = 3A \qquad V_{tpd} = IR = 3 \times 2 = 6V$

Therefore $P = 3 \times 6 = 18 \ W$ (3)

The student was *not* correct.

C6. The op. amp. question requires you to know:

(i) cell terminals

(ii) both + and - inputs are at *same* potential

(iii) $V_{\text{out}} = \dfrac{-R_f}{R_1} \cdot V_1$

You must be confident about y gain and timebase calculations on an oscilloscope.

(*a*) Inverting mode (1)

(*b*) (i) A zero (earthed)

(ii) B zero (same as + input)

(iii) C + 1·2V

(iv) $V_{\text{out}} = \dfrac{-5}{1} \times 1\cdot2 = -6\text{V}$ (Inverting mode) (3)

(*c*) (i) Gain $= \dfrac{V_{\text{out}}}{V_1}$ $V_{\text{out}} = 2 \times 5 = 10\text{V}$

$V_1 = 2 \times 0\cdot1 = 0\cdot2\text{V}$

$\Rightarrow$ Gain $= \dfrac{10}{0\cdot2} = 20$ (2)

(ii) $\dfrac{R_f}{1k\Omega} = 20 \Rightarrow R_f = 20k\Omega$ (1)

(iii) $f = \dfrac{1}{T}$

T $= 10 \times 1 = 10\text{ms} = \dfrac{10}{1000}s$

$\Rightarrow f = \dfrac{1000}{10} = 100\text{Hz}$ (2)

C7. Read your textbook or notes to see how holes and electrons combine in the pn junction to produce photons.

Remember the formulae $E = qV$

$$E = hf$$

and $\lambda = \dfrac{v}{f}$

(a) See note above. (1)

(b) $R = \dfrac{V}{I} = \dfrac{6 - 2\cdot 4}{0\cdot 020} = \dfrac{3\cdot 6}{0\cdot 020} = 180\,\Omega$ (2)

(c) The energy to create photons will be qV

$$\Rightarrow qV = hf$$

$$\Rightarrow f = \dfrac{qV}{h} = \dfrac{1\cdot 6 \times 10^{-19} \times 2}{6\cdot 63 \times 10^{-34}} = 4\cdot 83 \times 10^{14}\,\text{Hz}$$ (3)

(d) $\lambda = \dfrac{v}{f} = \dfrac{3 \times 10^{8}}{4\cdot 83 \times 10^{14}} = 6\cdot 21 \times 10^{-7}\,m\ (621\ nm)$

The light is red. (1)

C8. For a maximum in an interference pattern, the path difference must be a whole number of wavelengths ($n\lambda$).

(a) Interference (1)

(b) BY = 95·0 cm   AY = 89·2 cm.
The path difference for the 1st max = λ = 95·0 − 89·2
$\Rightarrow \lambda = 5\cdot 8$ cm (2)

(c) $f = \dfrac{V}{\lambda} = \dfrac{3 \times 10^{8}}{0\cdot 058} = 5\cdot 17 \times 10^{9}\,\text{Hz}$ (2)

Compare this with $5 \times 10^{9} \pm 10\%$
which means the acceptable range is from $4\cdot 5 \times 10^{9} \to 5\cdot 5 \times 10^{9}$. The value is acceptable.

C9. Equations to use in this question are $E = hf$;

$$A = \frac{N}{t}; \quad H = Dw_R; \quad D = \frac{E}{m}.$$

And remember that the annual effective dose for a member of the UK public in one year is approximately 2mSv.

(a) $E = hf = 6\cdot63 \times 10^{-34} \times 1\cdot6 \times 10^{20}$

$= 1\cdot6 \times 10^{-13}$ J   (2)

(b) (i) $A = \frac{N}{t} \Rightarrow N = At = 50 \times 10^3 \times 60 \times 60 = 1\cdot8 \times 10^8$ photons

but he only absorbs 20% of the photons $= 3\cdot6 \times 10^7$ photons   (2)

(ii) $H = Dw_R = \frac{E}{M} w_R = \frac{3\cdot6 \times 10^7 \times 1\cdot06 \times 10^{-13}}{60} \times 0\cdot9$

$= 5\cdot7 \times 10^{-8}$ Sv   (2)

(c) This value is about 35 thousand times smaller than the 2mSv annual effective dose. It should not raise too much concern.   (1)

C10. Half value thickness is the thickness required to reduce the measured activity to half its original value.

Induced fission requires to be 'triggered' by a neutron.
$E = mc^2$

(a) (i) The count rate is reduced from 184 to 92 by a thickness of 10 mm.

The half value thickness is 10   (1)

(ii) Rate μSvh^{-1} Thickness (mm)
     40    $\longrightarrow$ 0
     20    $\longrightarrow$ 10
     10    $\longrightarrow$ 20
     5     $\longrightarrow$ 30

A suitable thickness is 30 mm (3 half value thicknesses)   (2)

(b) (i) The reaction is induced. Spontaneous fission occurs without any external particle being involved. Induced fission requires a neutron to collide with the $_{22}^{235}u$ nucleus.   (1)

(ii) Element has mass number of 98 and an atomic (proton) number of 40. It is the element Zirconium Zr.   (1)

(iii) Mass before fission ($\times 10^{-25}$ kg)   Mass after fission ($\times 10^{-25}$ kg)

$$
\begin{array}{cc}
 & 2{\cdot}221 \\
3{\cdot}901 & 1{\cdot}626 \\
\underline{0{\cdot}017} & \underline{0{\cdot}068} \\
3{\cdot}918 & 3{\cdot}915
\end{array}
$$

$$E = mc^2 = 0{\cdot}003 \times 10^{-25} \times 9 \times 10^{16}$$
$$= 2{\cdot}7 \times 10^{-11} \text{J}$$ (3)